PLANNING PASSENGER RAILWAYS:
A Handbook

Edited by
Nigel G Harris
and
Ernest W Godward

Transport Publishing Co Ltd : Glossop : Derbyshire : England

Published by Transport Publishing Company
128 Pikes Lane
Glossop
Derbyshire
SK13 8EH

British Library Cataloguing in Publication Data

Planning Passenger Railways
  1. Railways
  I. Harris, N.G.   II. Godward, E.W.

Printed in Great Britain by
Transport Publishing Company
128 Pikes Lane
Glossop
Derbyshire
SK13 8EH

ISBN 0 86317 174 5

All black/white photographs are by the authors,
with colour photographs as attributed. Front cover
photograph by courtesy of British Rail.

Dedicated to the memory of
Natalie Lesley Godward (née Davies)
(1958-1990)

"All death is cruel – nothing is sadder than a blazing
fire suddenly being snuffed out."

This quote was taken from "With Open Heart" by Michel
Quoist, Gill & Macmillan (Dublin) 1983. It was the last book
that Natalie read before she died.

Contents

Acknowledgements

The inspiration for this book came from Natalie, Ernie's late wife, who tragically died from cancer in April 1990. It is to her memory that this book is dedicated. She persuaded Ernie that such a book was possible, and everything then flowed from a chance conversation between the editors.

A large number of people have helped us in the preparation of this volume. We are obviously indebted to all the authors for their time and effort in contributing to the book, particularly owing to the short time during which the book has been put together. However, their help would have been for nothing without the considerable input from John Senior of TPC in actually producing it, and from Amanda Askwith in helping to design the book to be readable and well set-out. Nigel's wife Alison provided substantial moral support, whilst we must also apologise to all our other friends and colleagues who have let us bore them with details of progress.

Whilst we have tried hard to ensure the factual accuracy of everything in this book, errors may have crept in (despite the attentions of ourselves and James Rodley, who proof-read the entire volume), and we are solely responsible for these, especially as all the contributions have been edited. Despite any such, we believe this to be a useful contribution to the important subject of planning railways, and we recommend it to you.

Nigel G Harris
Crystal Palace,
London SE19.

Ernest W Godward
Great Bromley,
Essex.

September 1991

Foreword

Transport is becoming a key issue. Much has happened in recent years, with significant changes in demand, technological advances (especially in computing and information technology), and increases in both road congestion and environmental awareness. Railways are moving up the agenda within the transport scene but, due to the expensive capital involved, and the long lead times in their construction, planning is particularly important.

Nevertheless, it is some years since a book was written on transport planning, and even that did not focus on the rail mode. Time is therefore ripe for an up-to-date text. This book covers the major themes and concerns in the planning of modern passenger railways - from creating the vision right through to issues of implementation. Major sections cover policy, demand and operational analysis, engineering, environmental and financial issues. Within these headings, the volume contains practical contributions in planning the main elements of track, structures, trains, stations and the operating organisation behind the scenes. Examples from throughout Britain and, indeed, elsewhere, have been described by colleagues within the rail industry, including consultants, practitioners and academics. I recommend it to you.

Denis Tunnicliffe,
Managing Director,
London Underground Limited.

1. Introduction

Nigel G Harris

Importance of Planning
Planning is essential for all organizations, particularly those such as railways which are capital-intensive and where project lead-times are long. A number of procedures can be used to plan transport, either starting at a strategic level and working downwards, or looking at detailed problems and seeing how these relate to each other; this issue has recently been well described by Coombe[4,5,6]. The applicability of each is dependent on the role of the studies concerned (see Fig. 2 of Coombe[5]). For example, for railway investment purposes, planning needs to occur at a fairly disaggregate level, since both demand and capacity vary significantly across the network. However, at a strategic level, a top-down approach is required, and demand characteristics are of lesser importance.

Objectives of Railway Planning
The objectives of planning any new railway should be to develop and achieve the most cost-effective and appropriate system which will convey the required numbers of passengers to their desired destinations:

- safely
- reliably
- in a user-friendly, reasonably comfortable, clean, attractive and environmentally-acceptable manner
- with competitive total journey times and fares
- at minimum total capital, operating and maintenance life cycle costs

at the maximum rate at which they present themselves.

Structure of this Book
This book attempts to provide an introduction to a variety of passenger railway planning problems, ranging throughout the spectrum from strategic to detailed. We have attempted to cover the key areas of planning activity, ranging from economics to engineering, at a level which will serve both as a useful introduction to students of the subject,

9

and as a reminder of basic concepts to practitioners. We have also attempted to include examples from a variety of situations within the UK and, where possible, abroad, and chapter 10 discusses some of the issues that may differ with varying organisational structure.

Most of the key modelling techniques available are mentioned in this volume, and we have made a particular effort to supply references to enable further study on these more technical issues. Modelling is becoming an increasingly important part of planning, as it enables the effects of different demand levels and capacities to be tested without incurring significant expense. The results of modelling are measured in a variety of ways, and are discussed in a chapter on appraisal.

Nevertheless, the various activities which may be subsumed under the heading "Planning" are not random; there is a general procedure to follow, and the structure of this book, as set out in Fig. 1.1, follows the idealised sequence of planning for railways as we see it. There are six main groups of activities:

(i) policy issues, which ought to come first;
(ii) demand estimation;
(iii) engineering issues;
(iv) operability issues;
(v) environmental issues;
(vi) appraisal.

Consideration of ii - v can occur simultaneously, as illustrated, and indeed should do so in order to quicken the planning process.

In practice, of course, this procedure is often not followed (see, for instance, chapter 14). Resources may become available which give rise to a temporary window of opportunity for development; however, this opportunity-led approach can have its downfall if the *raison d'être* of planning railways - to provide changes in services to passengers - is ignored. For instance, it is all too tempting to say "There is a disused rail alignment; let's reopen it" without really considering whether it will perform a useful function in the railway network of the future; in some cases, the cart has dragged the horse, and policy has been determined by opportunity.

A more common deviation from the idealised plan is the iterative solution, often driven by costs. The desired outcome lands up being too expensive for the resources available, so the different issues all have to be revisited - can costs be reduced? or, less commonly, can demand estimates reasonably be increased? A classic case of the former was the deletion of two stations, and the substitution of a cheaper Class 142 'Pacer' railbus for the larger and more comfortable Sprinter unit being

acquired as part of the development of the Cardiff - Maesteg service due
to open in October 1992.

Key Concepts

There are are a number of key concepts which underlie transport
planning, and need to be discussed before proceeding further.

The first is the concept that **travel is a derived demand** i.e. that it is
consumed as a means to achieving some other function such as going to
work, shopping etc.; there are few railways which are supported
primarily by tourists purely seeking the ride (although BR's Settle-
Carlisle line, and the Welsh narrow-gauge lines fall into this category).
Because of the inherent differences in activities (e.g. going to work leads
to earning money, whilst going shopping involves spending it), journey
purpose is a key determinant of travel behaviour.

A person must expend both time and money in order to travel; the
overall package of disutilities is combined into the composite index of
the second key concept of **generalised cost (g.c.)**. It is usually assumed
that passengers act so as to minimise the disutility of travelling, where
disutility is measured by generalised cost in the form:

$$GC = f + b_0 + b_1 A + b_2 W + b_3 R,$$

where f = fare   A = access time
       W = waiting time R = running (in-vehicle) time
       b_0 = error term b_1, b_2, b_3 = weighting coefficients.

Because passengers value time spent in the different ways differently,
weightings are conventionally applied to the time elements. By
multiplying either the generalised times or the fare spent by Values Of
Time (VOT) (for which standard figures are available[13]), generalised
cost can be expressed in either units of money or time; a common unit is
required. Other attributes can be added to the generalised cost equation
if data is available. Revealed Preference experiments (see chapter 6) can
be used to determine passengers' relative weightings and, since b_3 is
conventionally set to be equal to one, the equation can be solved for a
particular situation. The relative weightings are of considerable
importance; for instance, if $b_1 = 2b_3$, then passengers are twice as
responsive to improvements in access time as they are for journey time
improvements, and operators need to pay attention to such a fact. In
fact, this is generally the case; b_1 and b_2 usually are twice b_3.

Note also that the error term includes elements which are
independent of time e.g. there is a disutility associated with changing
trains, irrespective of the time penalty incurred, and interchange

11

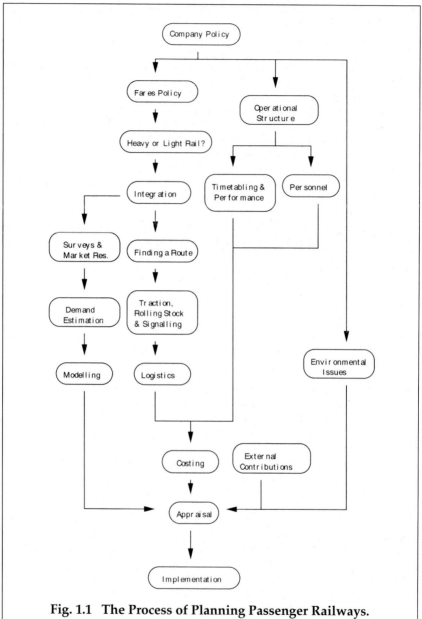

Fig. 1.1 The Process of Planning Passenger Railways.

penalties of up to 30 minutes have been identified for some market segments. Access issues can be somewhat separate, and the reader is advised to refer to the section on park-and-ride in chapter 5.

The third key concept is that of **elasticity**. An elasticity is defined as:

$$\frac{\text{proportionate change in y}}{\text{proportionate change in x}} = \frac{\dfrac{\triangle y}{y}}{\dfrac{\triangle x}{x}}$$

where x is the independent variable within the control of the operator. The most commonly-used elasticity measure is the fares elasticity, values of which are generally negative, since increasing fares leads *ceteris paribus* to reduced demand. Typical values for rail elasticities are given by journey purpose in Table 1.1, but it should be noted that elasticities are situation-specific, and great care should be taken if using these figures without independent verification, or at fare levels substantially different (say >10%) of the fare level at which they were calibrated.

Commuting	-0.5
Business	-0.4
Shopping	-0.8
Visiting Friends & Relatives	-1.1

Table 1.1 Typical British Rail Fare Elasticities

A detailed exposition of fares elasticities is beyond the scope of this book, and they are discussed in much greater depth elsewhere (ch. 7 of [15;1]). Nevertheless, readers should be familiar with the difference between point elasticities and arc elasticities. The elasticity defined above is the point elasticity, which is the gradient of the demand curve at a particular point; this underscores the importance of quoting elasticities with an absolute value, a time (e.g. year), and the environment in which measured, since they vary with all three. Arc elasticities are the gradient of a chord linking two points on the demand curve, and are therefore directly measurable (e.g. between two fare levels); they are, of course, equal to the equivalent point elasticity in the limiting condition, but are more appropriate for larger changes in the independent variable.

However, other elasticities are also used for planning purposes, particularly the service elasticity, which relates the level of generalised cost to demand; again, values are generally negative, since increasing generalised cost makes a service less attractive, and therefore the demand falls. Individual elements within the umbrella of generalised cost (such as waiting) also have their own elasticities (see, for instance, ch. 8 of [15], but these do not add up to the overall g.c. elasticity, even if all the g.c. elements are known, unless the weighting coefficients are all equal. However, it should be noted that it is not always possible to change variables independently; for instance, railway electrification may lead to increases in comfort as well as speed and frequency, and there is usually a residual increase in demand of 5-10% due to such a "sparks" effect.

The fourth key concept is the **trip matrix**. Data on trips between zonal origins and destinations conventionally stored in matrix form for the time-period under consideration, with traffic originating from the zones represented in the rows and having destinations in the column zones. Trips may also be found in the leading diagonal edge, and these are known as intra-zonal trips. For simplification, not all origins and destinations may be considered separately, and similar places may be treated together. For example, in studies of the UK, Northern Ireland might be treated as one zone; trips wholly within Northern Ireland would therefore be intra-zonal trips. The level of zonal disaggregation can therefore affect results, and increasing levels of disaggregation lead to decreasing levels of intra-zonal traffic.

Forecasting methods need to take into account whether the independent variables inherently affect origins or destinations. For instance, in the a.m. peak, when the predominant journey purpose is travel to work, increases in employment would be fed through into the trip matrix by multiplying column values ('factoring'), but for the p.m. peak, where the reverse is the case, employment growth would be catered for by factoring the rows.

Key Assumptions

Transport is a relatively young area of scientific inquiry, so there are a number of issues as yet not fully explored, and assumptions are commonly made as to their effects, so as to minimise problem size. Whilst problems of model under-specification (i.e. leaving out important determining variables) can arise unless due caution is taken, some of the usual key assumptions are discussed below.

First, trips are often assumed to be **single-purpose**. This is a reasonable assumption for modelling the a.m. peak but, at other times of day, many people make linked trips (e.g. going shopping on the way home, rather than going home directly). This makes the allocation of trips to a trip purpose (and hence prediction of future trends) difficult. 30% of trips have been found to be multi-purpose[7].

Secondly, the **attributes of passengers** (e.g. their response to interchange) are often assumed to be the same across all passengers. Whilst it is possible to vary elasticities by O-D pair (subject to data being available), walking and waiting time weightings are usually assumed equal for all trips, even though this is patently not the case for passengers of differing mobilities with differing amounts of luggage.

Thirdly, as has been noted[11], once travel decisions are taken, behaviour becomes **habitual**. Habits, thresholds and resistance to change lead to discontinuities in the demand curve, until choices are re-evaluated. This may occur through (a) dissatisfaction with service, (b) unsolicited information from marketing activities, (c) changes in home or job location, or (d) changes in lifestyle e.g. having children. To this list one might also add car purchase and temporary but planned service reductions (e.g. the deliberate closure of part of London King's Cross station in 1988 in order to replace fire-damaged escalators).

Fourthly, the model assumes **perfect passenger knowledge**. Whilst one might reasonably assume that commuters are indeed aware of alternatives, this is becoming less the case as people move house more frequently, and such an assumption is much weaker in relation to offpeak travellers. The severity of this assumption can, nevertheless, be reduced by probabilistic, rather than deterministic, planning; however, the extent to which the other options considered are sub-optimal, and how many passengers are assumed to use them remain somewhat arbitrary.

Moreover, a knowledge of alternatives requires effort (the generalised cost of obtaining information is not zero, as it is in the economists' perfect market), and individuals will only invest the effort if, in economic terms, the perceived gains in their utility are large enough. Marketing can, however, be used to limit the "laggedness" of passenger response.

The extent to which passengers mis-perceive attributes of rail services has been investigated by a number of authors, who have commonly found that car users over-estimate the disutility of travelling by rail (or, for that matter, other public transport modes). Reference 7 summarizes the work of others[2,12,14] in examining passenger perception; more recent work, but with similar conclusions, has been reported by Harris[9].

15

Factors Not Included

A number of factors are often considered to be outside the scope of railway planning *per se*. These variables include:

- the attractiveness of particular cities as centres for commerce, tourism or any other purpose (an issue for land-use planners, but usually an assumption for transport planners);
- changes in land or property values (ditto);
- safety on the rail network (except insofar as severe overcrowding is included as a time deterrent);
- the environment (either in terms of noise or pollution);
- road safety ; or
- improved passenger comfort in new rolling stock that is introduced over the forecasting period, although SP experiments (see chapter 6) have been conducted recently to quantify this.

Occasionally, these factors may be crucial in determining the demand for rail transport, even away from those situations where travel is consumed for its own sake. For instance, one study[3] showed that the scenery of the Exmouth-Exeter route was an important influence in the mode choice decision between car, bus and train. Moreover, passengers may perceive some of these issues to be important e.g. safety. Safety has not been included in this book, not because it is unimportant, but because it has been taken as given, and legal protection is now given to a variety of situations where safety could be prejudiced.

Land-use planning and transport planning matters are often closely related, in what should be an iterative process. Too often, however, councils responsible for land-use planning do not take into account the local railway network (which is generally centrally-funded), unlike the local highway network, which is more often under their control. Railways may therefore find themselves running through an area which is run-down (e.g. Middlesbrough - Redcar on BR) or an area not suitable for development; the high fixed costs of rail construction (see reference 10 and chapter 17) may leave the railways in a difficult financial position. Strategic land-use planning, taking account of the railways' ability to move large numbers of passengers, is relatively rare, but Hall's major work on land-use and transport planning in the South-East of England[8] is a significant exception. This book has assumed that overall strategic and land-use planning matters are not within the scope of most railways to affect directly (although railway operators can hope to be included as part of the consultation process).

References

1. Association of Metropolitan Authorities and Department of Transport (1984), Technical Seminar on Public Transport Demand Elasticities, Transport Studies Unit, University of Oxford.
2. Chen, D.H., Parker, J. & Richards, M.J. (1975) "Perception-Based Modal Split Modelling", Centre for Transport Studies, Cranfield Institute of Technology.
3. Cook, H. & Pope, J. (1982) Attitudes and Beliefs of Rail and Non-Rail Users to Modal Choice between Exmouth and Exeter, Plymouth Polytechnic, Dept. of Shipping & Transport Working Paper 5.
4. Coombe, D. (1990) Urban Transport Strategy Development: Top-down or Bottom-up?, *Transpn. Planning Systs.* 1 pp. 3-10.
5. Coombe, D. (1991a) Urban Transport Strategy Development, *Traff. Engng. & Ctrl.* 32 pp. 9-11.
6. Coombe, D. (1991b) Practical Urban Transport Strategy Development, *Traff. Engng. & Ctrl.* 32 pp. 176-185.
7. Goodwin, P.B. & Hensher, D.A. (1978) "The Transport Determinants of Travel Choices: An Overview", ch. 1 in Hensher, D.A. & Dalvi, Q. "Determinants of Travel Choice".
8. Hall, P. (1989) "London 2001".
9. Harris, N.G. (1987) "Perception of Provincial Rail Services", *Modern Rlys.* 44 p.14.
10. Harris, N.G. (1988) "Dependence on the Past", *Modern Rlys.* 45 pp. 309-311.
11. Hensher, D.A. (1975) "Perception and Commuter Mode Choice: an Hypothesis", *Urban Studies* 50 no. 1.
11. Liivamagi, P. (1974) "Perception of Travel Times", Transport Studies Group, University College London (unpublished).
12. MVA Consultancy, ITS Leeds University and TSU Oxford University (1987), "The Value of Travel Time Savings", Policy Journals.
13. O'Farrell, P.N. & Markham, J. (1974) "Commuter Perceptions of Public Transport Work Journeys", *Envt. & Plng.* A 16.
14. Transport & Road Research Laboratory (1980) "The Demand for Public Transport".

2. Strategic and Business Planning for Railways

Hugh L Sumner

Introduction

It is difficult to generalise about the best strategy for railways. Not only do rail systems and the environments in which they operate differ greatly, but different sets of directors and policy-makers can set varying objectives within the same scenario. Nevertheless, there are a number of key issues which need to be addressed, and this chapter sets out a case study in which these are discussed.

In addition to the example of London Underground set out below, however, there is a considerable amount of literature on policy issues, including a complete book on the strategic change in BR's ScotRail division in the mid 1980s[14]. A number of other railways have pursued strategic planning techniques in order to change their business fundamentally, and these have been reported in keynote speeches[11,12], interviews[9] and published papers. These latter have included papers on Netherlands Railways[15], Australia[7], Austria[13] and Spain[1] as well as on British Rail[6,8]. Similar strategies may also be developed for all modes in an urban area where rail may be one of several public transport modes (see, for instance, [5]). In addition, on an even wider plane, some general business planning books can provide useful suggestions for the railway planner (e.g. [2,4,10]).

Case Study: London Underground

STRATEGIC PLANNING or - "When Noah started building the Ark it wasn't raining"

The urban travel market in which mass transit systems in general (and London Underground Ltd. (LUL) in particular) operate can be characterized as being:

- high volume, but of low individual trip value which, with the exception of the car, diplays little brand loyalty

- has in the past been considered by both supplier and buyer almost as a distress purchase, from suppliers operating in a semi-monopolistic environment
- subject to major peaks and troughs of demand: day, week and year
- expanding, changing rapidly and very diverse in terms of modes, users and usage
- becoming more fragmented as competition increases.

The net result of these influences is that competition is increasing rapidly - the customer really does count.

Strategic planning within the context of such a mass transit system thus seeks to match the requirements and capabilities of the business with the needs of the customer over extremely long timescales. It thus:

- defines and drives the scope of an organisation and its activities
- fits and matches the organisation's activities to the future environment
- acquires and matches resources to activities
- allocates or reallocates resources to suit the desired and agreed goal(s) set
- sets up internal and external values and expectations
- determines the long term direction of the company and its response(s) to competition
- drives the internal organisation structure and workings of the business.

The planning cycle itself consists of a natural chain of events as set out in Fig. 2.1; each has feedback loops and interactive cycles within each element.

Such a process can, in classical planning theory, be either an incremental or a step-change process. The incrementalist continuously adjusts strategic policies and directions as the market and environment changes. Conversely the proponents of step-change planning wait longer between major changes in direction, arguing that short term adjustments confuse the organisation and do not reflect real long term shifts within the planning environment. In the case of LUL a balance has historically been struck between occasional major strategic reviews and continued adjustment through such mechanisms as the annual business plan.

The last major review of strategy and use of such a process within the Underground was in 1988 following a major shift in the planning environment.

THE 1988 PLANNING ENVIRONMENT or - "there are rainclouds building in the west"

Prior to 1988 the last significant review of strategy by the Company occurred in 1982 and in the period between these plans significant shifts had occurred across a number of dimensions of the business:
- market volume, share and usage
- legislative environment
- safety performance
- internal efficiency and effectiveness
- funding regime and asset health

Each of these changes and imperatives influenced the shape of the plan.

In terms of customers, the Underground had experienced a significant and continued loss of trade since the late 1950's. The nadir of its fortunes occurred in 1982 when the business carried 600 million trips per annum. In the years following 1982 a 60% increase in usage

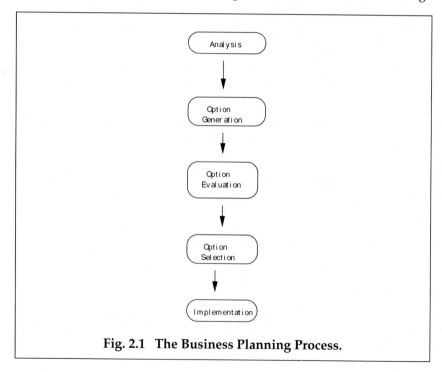

Fig. 2.1 The Business Planning Process.

occurred leading to problems with crowding, congestion and travel comfort. Unfortunately, the 1982 strategic plan, and its subsequent revisions in the annual business plans, failed to predict this increase in usage: a step change was now overdue.

During this six year period between major plans the legislative environment changed significantly: the 1984 London Regional Transport Act created LUL as a limited subsidiary company of London Regional Transport. The Act whilst laying down general duties to the travelling public and the co-ordination of services also put a requirement on the business to prove, as in Local Government, the cost effectiveness of its internal contracting and works units. As a result the company had restructured and split the role of specifier/requirer and do-er within the engineering environment.

In the lead-up to 1988 significant efforts had been made to improve efficiency of service delivered to the customer, e.g. through the one person operation of trains. However, these were primarily focussed on cost minimisation rather than quality and value maximisation; it was believed, however, that as the basis of competition and service delivery changed towards quality that the company would need to alter its focus.

Lastly, whilst there had been significant investment over the years in new infrastructure only a limited amount of funding had been directed at maintaining an increasingly aged infrastructure and coping with the burgeoning demand.

It was within this planning environment that a new strategic plan was crafted.

PLANNING PROCESS & TOOLS or - "what does the seaweed say?"

The planning process looked at both the internal and external factors which would drive the Company forward or influence its direction. Only then could a series of strategic options be developed.

Analysis of internal and external factors was run in parallel, with the modelling of internal factors focussing on such aspects as;

- the impact of changes in opening hours
- the quantity and quality of service delivered
- the size of the network and impact of crowding on customer usage
- new lines and extensions

A vital tool in this process was the use of LUL's rail network model (see chapter 9) linked to a financial evaluation model.

21

Analysis of the internal capabilities of the Company looked to establish sensible boundaries and derive fundamental relationships between cost, income, investment and demand. External factors to be considered and analysed included:

- market position and competing modes
- buyers, suppliers, new entrants and substitute products
- base demand forecasts
- likely changes in the legislative environment

In addition, the view of the outside environment was directed at developing a realistic range of demand forecasts split into three categories: peak, off-peak and weekends. These demand scenarios took account of:

- the relationship between supply and demand for services
- changing demographic and employment profiles at a borough and county level
- forecast increases in real disposable income and thus propensity to use the service
- increased consumer spending and changes in the leisure, domestic and foreign tourist markets

On top of these demand scenarios were factored potential impacts from changes in work patterns and changes in legislation eg the Unified Business Rate. Based on this analysis it was forecast that there would be an increase in latent demand of 20% and 30% in the peak and off-peak respectively over a ten year timeframe. The forecast increase in demand allied to the need to consider all forms of public transport resulted in the setting up of a joint study with British Rail, London Regional Transport and the Department of Transport: the Central London Rail Study[3].

As a result of this analysis five key strategic issues were identified:

1. passenger volumes exceeded capacity, which could only be enhanced slowly;
2. commercial performance had improved, but much remained to be done;
3. the structure and management capabilites needed adjustment;
4. significant investment would be required under any scenario, even to keep the asset base at its present condition; and

5. quality and safety standards must be improved if the customer base was to be retained.

These immediate issues were in turn exacerbated by the forecast growth in demand.
To meet the five strategic issues four different strategic options were developed, building from the boundary testing completed in the first stage. These options ranged from an expanded network carrying large volumes of customers, to a more commercial and financial driven business. No one option was clearly superior, but key elements of them were combined to form a single strategic direction. The selected strategy was then tested for its sensitivity - for the future never materialises as predicted.

STRATEGIC DIRECTION or - "It's going to rain - build a boat"

The selected strategic direction had three major five year phases designed to address the issues in a logical sequence:
Phase 1 focussed on internal management reform, service quality and safety improvement and securing sound financial performance. This phase was designed to provide a firm foundation for the later phases. Significant funding was proposed for safety improvements and in the basic health of the existing asset base.
Phase 2 (the second five years) consolidated on the first stage with further improvements in facilities, quality and reliability. In this phase capacity was to be brought on stream to cope with demand in the central area and congested corridors into London.
Phase 3 (the third five years) looked towards expanding the system to tap new market opportunities.
This phased approach provided the flexibility to accelerate, merge or delay the phases and hence reflect fluctuations in the market and financing.

IMPLEMENTATION

Implementation of the plan has proceeded well, albeit with individual elements accelerated (for example, a Bill for the construction of the Jubilee line extension (a phase 3 item) was already in Parliament at the time of writing).
The Company split the role of the Chairman and Chief Executive and instead of one single operating department created ten line business units based on the individual underground lines. To provide a focal

point for the major restoration of the network and manage the design of new capacity - stations and lines - a separate development department was instituted.

The first major thrust of the Company was to tackle safety and, as a result, a single high-calibre professional group was set up, and an internationally-recognised safety management system adopted. This safety drive was supplemented a year later by starting a major quality initiative: a combination of Total Quality procedures and improvements in the assets (e.g. refurbishing the existing fleet of trains).

The third element of the change process has been the acceleration of schemes for improving the capacity of the network: the Jubilee Line extension to Stratford, Crossrail and potentially a new line between Chelsea and Hackney. This is in addition to making good the ravages of time on the existing infrastructure, though progress is being constrained because the investment needed for improvement far exceeds funds presently available.

GENERIC IMPLICATIONS OF STRATEGIC ALTERNATIVES

This chapter has focussed on the planning processes within London Underground Limited. However in general, regardless of the system or planning environment, there exists a range of outcomes that will provide a variety of satisfactory solutions ranging from:

- networks requiring low capital cost, providing adequate quality and safety carrying a relatively low volume of customers at high fares

to the other extreme of

- high investment, high quality, low fares networks carrying very large numbers of customers.

Whichever strategic alternative is adopted implications exist for the strategic planning, design and operation of networks across a wide range of dimensions:

Demand and Planning

The long timescales associated with the design, construction and operation of new lines require that

- sensitivity analysis becomes an integral part of the planning process;
- the strategies adopted are sufficiently flexible to allow for change as the future unfolds;

- fundamental market research is crucial; and
- quick and decisive action based on changing circumstances is vital given the long leadtime for system development.

Financial

- maximising the output from the existing asset base will in general provide a greater return than massive new capital investment in new lines;
- initial capital cost design must recognise that later expansion through anything other than by purchasing more rolling stock can be prohibitively expensive;
- operational and capital costs must be minimised if commercial borrowing or equity is to be employed; and
- private contribution from developers and other beneficiaries is essential rather than optional in today's environment.

Business and Operational

- speed of response to the market is vital;
- competition will be increasingly based on quality rather than cost, thus driving the need to integrate the production and marketing elements of the business;
- information on customer needs, attitudes and movements is becoming more essential;
- the human interface between server and served must be properly designed and managed;
- fares and operational systems must be designed to balance load and capacity across the network both spatially and temporally; and
- for existing capacity-constrained systems market penetration allied to product extension strategies are of more value than market extension.

Technological and Design

- interconnectivity between systems (see chapter 14) must be maximised to harness the "network effect", where improvements in two elements can provide benefits greater than the sum of doing them individually;
- technology must be put to competitive use in terms of system performance, operational/maintenance flexibility, customer and management information and the general travelling environment;
- the design of new lines must allow for

- ease of upgrading of both fixed and moving infrastructure;
- appropriate maintenance in terms of facilities and available skills;
- the increasingly rapid change in technology;
- global sourcing must be adopted to tap the new technology available, and
- counter increasing supplier concentration; and
- an explicit choice must be made between the risks and benefits of new technologies, or whether to stick with older but proven methods.

References

1. Carbajo, J.C. & de Rus, G. (1991) "Railway Transport Policy in Spain", *Jnl. Trans. Econ. & Pol.* 25 pp. 209-215.
2. Davidson, J.H. (1972) "Offensive Marketing", Penguin Books, Middlesex, England.
3. Department of Transport, British Rail Network SouthEast, London Regional Transport & London Underground Ltd. (1989) "Central London Rail Study".
4. Johnson, G. & Scholes, K. (1984) "Exploring Corporate Strategy", Prentice Hall International, London.
5. Jones, D., May, T. & Wenban-Smith, A. (1990), "Integrated Transport Studies: Lessons from the Birmingham Study", *Traff. Engng. & Ctl.* 31 pp. 572-576.
6. Nash, C.A. (1984) "Rail Policy in Britain - What Next?", *Transpn.* 12 pp. 243-259.
7. Nash, C.A. (1985) "Rail Policy and Performance in Australia", *Transp. Rev.* 5 pp. 289-300.
8. Nash, C.A. (1988) "British Rail and the Administration of Subsidies", ch. 6 pp. 90-105, in Whitehead, C. (ed) "Reshaping the Nationalised Industries", Policy Journals.
9. Pettitt, G. (1990) "Provincial into Regional: What's in a Name?", *Mod. Rlys.* 47 pp. 635-639.
10. Porter.M.E. (1980) "Competitive Strategy: Techniques for Analyzing Industries and Competitors", The Free Press, MacMillan Publishing Co. Inc., New York.
11. Prideaux, J.D.C.A. (1989) "InterCity: Passenger Railway Without Subsidy", Lecture given to the Royal Society for the Arts, London, 24th May.
12. Reid, R. (1990) "Preparing British Rail for the 1990s", presentation given to the Chartered Institute of Transport, London, 8th January.
13. Schonback, W. Brotholer, J. & Winkelbauer, S. (1990) "The 'New Railway' Concept in Austria", *Jnl. Trans. Econ. & Pol.* 24 pp. 219-226.
14. Stewart, V. & Chadwick, V. (1987) "Changing Trains", David & Charles, Newton Abbot, 190pp.
15. Waller, P. (1990) "Towards 2000 in the Netherlands", *Mod. Rlys.* 47 pp. 188-195.

3. Fares Policy & Logit Models

Nigel G Harris

The Need to Maximise Profit

In most countries with market economies, public transport has been under increasing financial pressure in recent years. Examples where public transport fares have deliberately held down are few and far between, but see ref. 8. More usually, a certain amount of cost reduction has often occurred, with the closure of lightly-used railway branch lines, for instance, but further improvements in financial performance are becoming increasingly difficult in the light of increasing car ownership and selected road developments. In order to survive, many railway managements are now paying particular attention to their pricing policy, as price elasticities are sometimes nearer zero than -1, although railway fares are often limited by political decisions as well as managerial ones.

Fare Systems and Modal Competition : Pricing and Distance

Flat fare systems have been shown not to be revenue-maximising[18], and are certainly not cost-minimising, since the marginal costs of passengers travelling further are not reflected in marginal revenue; flat fares are usually justified in terms of accessibility or simplicity. Distance-based systems certainly have a measure of cost-relatedness, but fares become so large over long distances that patronage levels are often artificially low, as occurs on DB (German Railways) for rail trips between (say) München and Hamburg.

Zonal fare systems attempt to combine the advantages of the other two systems, in maintaining a reasonable degree of simplicity whilst having some relation to costs incurred, but season tickets issued in such an environment can lead to substantial extra travel being made for no extra fare. The introduction of Travelcards in London is estimated to have increased demand by approx 13% within four years[13], but the advantages to passengers (and to operators in lower ticketing costs) have been at least partially offset by significant increases in congestion.

The Travelcard issue is a complex one, beyond the scope of this chapter, and readers are advised to refer elsewhere[6,20].

To understand this further, one must understand the competitive pressures of rail passenger demand, and the manner in which these apply through elasticities. Over very short distances (under 10km), competition from bus, cycle, car and even walking is intense, and elasticities are high (except in areas of severe road congestion when this competitive threat is limited). This problem is exacerbated by rail's high terminal costs, and the fact that trains tend to accelerate more slowly than their competitors, so that slow local rail services are rarely competitive. Rail therefore has high costs and an unattractive product in this environment; competitive forces would suggest low fares, but the high cost of carrying the traffic on offer usually makes this an unattractive option. Over very long distances, however (say over 500km), air travel is a particularly-strong alternative, given its enhanced line speed, but the marginal costs to the rail operator of the extra distance are low, and hence the extra marginal fares here tend to be much lower than average ones. Moreover, there is some evidence that large fares in monetary terms can also dissuade passengers from travelling[17]. The net result is the classic fare comprised of a boarding element, followed by fares which rise less than proportionately with distance. This is a simple situation, easily understood in economic and diagrammatic terms; revenue is maximised at a price elasticity of -1, but profit is maximised at a more negative price elasticity, since fewer passengers travelling will, *ceteris paribus*, lead to lower costs (see Figs. 3.1 & 3.2). (Note also that quantum leaps occur in fixed costs (e.g. when new tracks are required) but are not shown here.)

Pricing and Journey Purpose

Research has long shown that passengers' responses to fares differ by journey purpose; this is a direct corollary of the fact that travel is generally a derived demand (see chapter 1). Work is a necessary evil for most adults, and they get paid for it; travelling to work is therefore something that people generally will do, even if it is associated with a high disutility in terms of time and cost (fare), as long as the cost of travel remains relatively small in relation to the benefits from work (the wages) (If this is not the case, a change in job, even to the extent of deliberately remaining unemployed, may result). On the other hand, travel for leisure purposes is also not necessary, and trips are suppressed when economic downturns set in, since the general public has less disposable income. Railway income is significantly affected by the prevailing economic conditions, which is an important reason why BR's financial performance improved markedly in the late 1980s[3].

Pricing for the Peak : Variation in Elasticities Between Time-Periods

If fares are to be related, however roughly, to costs incurred in service provision, however, then some account must be taken of peak demand. Peak demands on public transport may be in the range of twice to ten times the prevailing offpeak demand, and specific resources are often used only in the peak e.g. trains may make only one single trip in each peak, lying idle for the rest of the day. In order to recover the capital costs of capacity used only in the peak, higher fares are justified. The traditional peak time of demand is based on the journey to work and, fortunately, demand elasticities are lower here, because (a) road congestion is worse (and hence alternative modes of travel are poorer), and (b) journey to work is the predominant journey purpose. Many transit operators, especially in the USA, have used time-of-day pricing for work peaks[5] ; see also ref. 16, esp. section 12.2.4.

In special circumstances, however, peaks may occur at other times e.g. on sporting occasions, on Summer Saturdays in holiday resorts, on Saturdays before Christmas in major shopping areas, etc. Particular problems arise when different peaks coincide; for instance, London's railway termini are especially busy on Friday evenings, when the evening work peak coincides with the weekend-away leisure peak and the (small) business week-away peak. Railways with different peaks, however, can use their capacity to great effect; spreading capacity costs over the maximum number of passengers allows an operator either to make large profits, or to reduce fares and increase mode share, or both. This is precisely the reason for the success of BR's Great Western InterCity services, which were built up on leisure and some business traffic, but where long-distance commuting became popular (and very profitable) after the introduction of HSTs[1].

There is thus an *a priori* case for varying fares by time-period, although there can be certain difficulties associated with defining the time-periods (for instance, it is difficult to stop offpeak passengers travelling when the evening peak starts; moreover, research has shown that the benefits of introducing evening peak restrictions can be marginal.) Thus "the peak is priced to maximise revenue for minimum recession, and the offpeak is priced to encourage speculative trade"[15].

British Rail have recognised the importance of a simple business : leisure fares split since 1985, based on an open admission that "the railway needs to price its product in relation to its own costs and to what the market will bear at different times of the day and different

29

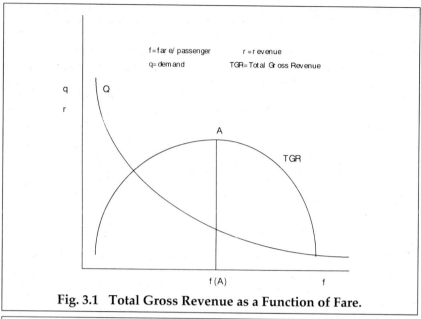

Fig. 3.1 Total Gross Revenue as a Function of Fare.

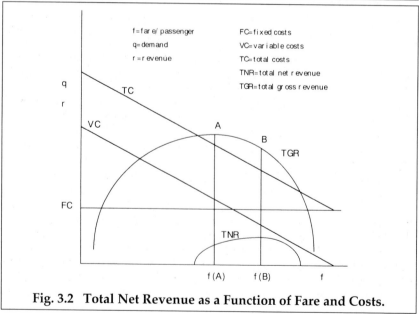

Fig. 3.2 Total Net Revenue as a Function of Fare and Costs.

points in the week"[2]. Its InterCity sector is among the leading practitioners of time-of-day pricing, with all trains allocated to one of three colour codings, with 'red' trains available only to passengers with the most expensive tickets, then 'white' trains, then 'blue' trains available to all passengers. These colour codings apply to days of the week as well as to individual trains on weekdays; 'blue' tickets are not available on Fridays, for instance, because of the coincidence of the work, business and leisure peaks.

Subject to the disadvantages of excessive complexity of administration and passenger understanding, any number of different fares can be introduced to segment the travel market by time of day (and, implicitly, by the types of passengers that are able to take advantage of the different times). The real problem is that revenue abstraction occurs, with passengers able to afford high fares switching to take advantage of lower fares, although this can be minimised by such concepts as the railcard, only available to certain easily-definable population segments with high fares elasticities (e.g. students, the over-65s).

For railways without pricing freedom, varying prices by time-of-day and/or by train may also have the advantage of increasing revenue without incurring Government wrath, since the basic fares are still available - but only at selected times. This may be further disguised by treating the higher fares as a supplement system, as is done in France.

Passenger Response to Time-Dependent Fares Levels

In the simple case of one fare payable per Origin:Destination pair, passengers have only two options within the mode: (a) travel and pay the fare charged; or (b) forego the trip by rail, either travelling by another mode or not at all. As more fares levels are introduced, however, passengers have an increasing range of options whilst still travelling by rail. For example, in the two-tier fares case, a passenger finding the higher-fare time-of-day expensive can either (a) travel at the preferred time and pay the fare charged; or (b) travel at another time but at a reduced fare; or (c) forego the trip by rail. The manner in which passengers make these decisions is of particular interest to railway managers, but is not straightforward to analyse.

Disaggregate Discrete Choice Modelling : Different Techniques Available

There are, however, a number of methods of analysing data from a limited number of options, as we have here (travel peak, travel offpeak or not at all), and these methods fall under the heading of discrete choice modelling. We are particularly interested here in the response of

31

individual passengers, since flows on individual Origin: Destination pairs are often small, but railway pricing can be done at this level. For rail passengers, the key variable is some measure of the difference in fare, although this can be measured in terms of an absolute difference or a multiplicative difference.

In a study carried out on two-tier fares on BR's local line on Teesside[10], four model types were considered: (i) linear regression; (ii) discriminant analysis; (iii) probit analysis; and (iv) logit analysis. The binary choice was seen to be whether to travel at peak (represented by the probability p(P)) or at offpeak times (represented by the probability p(O)). Semilog modelling (see, for instance, ref. 19) was rejected as being inferior to standard logit analysis.

Linear regression was rejected since it permits impossible probability values since it is unbounded[9] (p(P) and p(O) can both exceed 1 or fall below zero, which is unsatisfactory). Discriminant analysis was rejected since it is severely affected by outliers[12], which were present in most of the variables of interest. The two similar technqiques of probit and logit analysis seemed to be useful techniques; they are based on biological research where proportional, rather than absolute, changes in variables, are critical in determining outcomes (and this is similar to elasticity theory and public transport fares). The probability of being assigned to one category or the other is based on an S-shaped curve resulting from a dependent variable being a function of a linear combination of independent variables (see Fig 3.3). Probit was originally preferred to logit on grounds of easier computation and assumptions about the normal distribution of the random elements of the utility function, but logit has become more widely used in transport applications of late, particularly those involving yes : no decisions, as modern computers and proofs of logistically-distributed error terms have been developed.

However, care must be taken to avoid the logit model's deficiency of the IIA property (the Independence of Irrelevant Alternatives), which arises where there are more than two alternatives, and which casts doubt on model results where some pairs of alternatives are more similar than others. In a time-of-day modelling scenario, the introduction of Sunday services on a railway previously having none would cause problems, since the model formulation means that the ratio of Saturday: weekday traffic would stay the same, even though intuitively this is not necessarily so. Model respecification (e.g. by including more variables, or modelling different journey purposes separately) is the recommended solution[14]. Restricting the analysis of the Teesside data reported below to a binary decision removed the major weakness of previous work on cross-price commuter elasticities in the High Wycombe- and Bedford-London corridors[7], where the IIA property led to the assumption that, for each ticket type, cross-price elasticities with respect to the other ticket types were all equal, which is intuitively untrue.

Even after selecting a method of analysis, decisions still have to be made as to method of estimation. In recent times, the original methods of curve-fitting and weighted least squares have been replaced by more modern iterative techniques, with Maximum Likelihood (ML) being the current preference. ML produces estimators that are efficient, consistent and sufficient[11].

Further, a goodness-of-fit statistic is also required to show the performance of the model; rho-squared has been developed along similar lines to the R^2 conventionally used in assessing the performance of linear regression.

Logit Modelling: Nesting and Other Applications

As logit has become an accepted form of analysis, it has been developed both methodologically and in terms of its applications. The most important methodological development has been the nested logit model, where hierarchies of decisions can be modelled together; the mode choice decision hierarchy might be peak train : offpeak train within a bus : train decision within a car : public transport decision. This

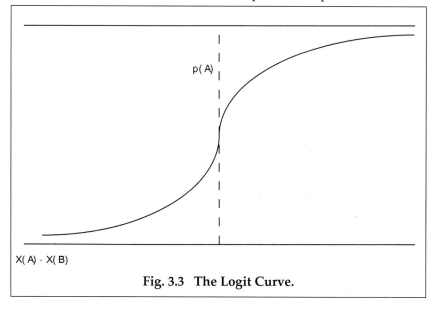

Fig. 3.3 The Logit Curve.

initial public: private transport decision has been widely used e.g. see ref. 4 and chapter 7. In another context, Doxsey[6] used a logit formulation in an analysis of the Travelcard : pay cash decision.

Application to Two-Tier Fares on Teesside

A data-set compiled from on-train surveys was reduced to remove through passengers from InterCity services, where travel restrictions were quite different, and the fares of a different order of magnitude, and Ranger-type tickets, where it is difficult to allocate a sensible fare to each single journey (a disadvantage in limiting this type of analysis to situations where Travelcard-type systems do not apply). Moreover, some grouping of values of the difference between peak and offpeak fares was necessary, in order to get enough (i.e. 30) values within each of the data-points used for the modelling exercise. Dummy variables were set up to examine the effects of the passenger not paying for the ticket him/herself (for example, if a company had paid, one would expect elasticities to be different). Other variables included distance, the absolute value of the fare, and differences in frequency and journey time between the peak and the off-peak. The statistical package SPSS-X was used to compute the estimated coefficients, although other programming environments (e.g. GLIM) are probably now superior.

Results

Fare structure variables were indeed shown to be much more statistically-significant than the other variables. A much better fit was achieved using ratio, as opposed to difference, measures of peak and offpeak fares, whilst the business-paying dummy variable was (unsurprisingly) significant in assigning non-work trips to the offpeak. Nevertheless, the level of explanation as shown by rho-squared was extremely disappointing at only 0.076 for the best single-variable model, and 0.122 for a model with four independent variables. However, one would expect rho-squared to increase with an increasing number of variables; the question is whether the increase is significant or not. Log-likelihoods are used to arbitrate this decision; for example, to be statistically-significant at the 5% level, the log-likelihoods must fall by at least 1.9 for an additional variable (values are taken from the chi-squared distribution, which log-likelihoods follow). In this study, a three-variable model with the peak:offpeak fares ratio, business dummy and absolute value of the peak fare was the preferred model on this basis.

There are, however, other criteria for model acceptance e.g. the number of data points wrongly allocated. Net misclassifications were around 20%; when data-points were unusual in some manner, the model allocated them to the larger category, which was offpeak.

The coefficients derived were then directly used in an algebraic analysis which yielded cross-price elasticity estimates. Logit analysis based solely on the absolute difference between fares gives

$$\beta_p = [1 + \exp(-b(P_o - P_p))]^{-1}$$

where β_p is the proportion of patronage accruing to the peak period. Differentiation yields

$$e_{po} = bP_o + e_o$$

and

$$e_{op} = bP_p + e_p,$$

where e_{po} is the cross-price elasticity of demand for peak travel with respect to offpeak fare etc. (for further details see ref. 10). Analysis of the results showed that the existing fares ratio was too small.

Problems

Even though elasticities appeared to be fairly high (thereby implying that other alternatives were available to passengers), the study did not take sufficient care with the problem of captives i.e. those passengers who are not able to switch between time-periods (most particularly, many peak passengers are constrained by their hours of employment). The study depended on estimates of own-price elasticities in the peak and offpeak periods, and this could easily have been remedied by examination of revealed preference data relating to the demand effects of previous fare increases. Also, the definitions of 'peak' and 'offpeak' were slightly confused by the non-existence of evening peak fare restrictions, thereby giving negative cross-price elasticities which, although correct in this particular circumstance, do not demonstrate an intuitive result of general significance.

Conclusions

Railway operators need to maximise revenue by the judicious use of fares policies relating fares both to costs and to elasticities. As new ticket technology comes into widespread use, data is improving and detailed studies can be carried out on a number of policy areas such as the ratio between peak and offpeak fares. A number of disaggregate modelling techniques are available, of which logit modelling is a popular one, which enable such analyses to be carried out.

References

1. Anon (1988) "Focus on Great Western InterCity into Profit", 12-page supplement issued with *Rail*.
2. BRB (1984) Annual Report and Accounts 1983.
3. BRB (1989) Annual Report and Accounts 1988/89.
4. de Cea, J., Ortuzar, J. de D. & Willumsen, L.G. (1986) "Evaluating Marginal Improvements to a Transport Network: an Application to the Santiago Underground", *Transpn.* 13 pp. 211-233.
5. Cervero, R. (1986) "Time-of-Day Transit Pricing: Comparative US and International Experiences", *Transp. Revs.* 6 pp. 347-364.
6. Doxsey, L.B. (1984) "Demand for Unlimited Use Transit Passes", *Jnl. Transp. Econ. & Pol. 18* pp. 7-22.
7. Glaister, S. (1983) "Some Characteristics of Rail Commuter Demand", *Jnl. Transp. Econ. & Pol. 17* pp. 115-132.
8. Goodwin, P.B. et al. (1983) "Subsidised Public Transport and the Demand for Travel".
9. Green, P.E., Carmone, F.J. & Wachspress, D.P. (1977) "On the Analysis of Qualitative Data in Marketing Research", *Jnl. Mkting. Res. 14* pp. 52-59.
10. Harris, N.G. (1988) "A Study of Rail Demand in a Two-Tier Fares Environment", *Jnl. Transp. Plng. & Tech.* 12, pp. 231-237.
11. Hosmer, D. & Lemeshow, S. (1980) "Goodness-of-Fit Tests for the Multiple Logistic Regression Model", *Comms. in Stats.: Theory and Methods* A9(10) pp. 1043-1049.
12. Jennrich, R. & Sampson, P. (1983) "Stepwise Discriminant Analysis".
13. London Transport (1987) "Traffic Trends Since 1970", Economic Research Report R266.
14. NCHRP (1982) "Application of Disaggregate Travel Demand Models", Transportation Research Board NCHRP Report 253.
15. Sephton, P.J. (1984) "Differential Bus Fares to Maximise Revenue", *PTOR 16th Sem. Proc.*, Univ. of Leeds pp. K1-K11.
16. Transport & Road Research Laboratory (1980) "The Demand for Public Transport".
17. Usher, J.B. (1984) "Rail Fares - Pricing for Segmentation", *PTOR 16th Sem. Proc.*, Univ. of Leeds pp. L1-L4.
18. Webster, F.V. (1976) "Fare Structure for Bus Stage Services", TRRL LR704.
19. Westley, G. D.(1979) "The Demand for Urban Rail Transportation", *Jnl. Am. Stat. Ass. 74*, pp. 576-587.
20. White, P.R. (1981) " 'Travelcard' Tickets in Urban Public Transport", *Jnl. Trans. Econ. & Pol.* 15 pp. 17-34.

4. Heavy or Light Rail?

Phil Haywood

Introduction

The key to determining the type of rail system to be used is having a full understanding of demand, including passengers' perceptions of the options[10]. It is only by having this understanding that an objective assessment can be made on whether investment in rail is justified and then in the type of rail technology to be employed. This chapter examines the criteria used to help in determining the choice of transport system and in particular why light rail is for many cities a more realistic option than heavy rail. It also suggests a few basic criteria and methods by which an initial indication of the most likely options can be gained.

Definitions of Heavy and Light Rail

Rail systems or rapid transit systems have been defined by the International Union of Public Transport (UITP) and by the Department of Transport (DTp) following the increased interest in light rail as a solution to urban transport problems. Although the DTp in a briefing note on Light Rapid Transit Systems[1] stated there are no strict legal definitions they offer the following:-

Railway: The normal urban and inter-urban railway as operated by national mainline railway operators carrying both passengers and freight. The passenger rolling stock is built to UIC standards (or better) and requires compatability of buffing and draw gear.

Heavy Rapid Transit: Similar technically to conventional rail, but usually understood to mean high capacity, frequent interval, electrified urban railways in an entirely segregated system, often underground, using heavy duty rolling stock. Some French-built rubber tyred Metro systems of this type use guideway technology. Systems have full signalling and conventional stations with platforms.

Light Rail or Light Rapid Transit (LRT): A guided transit system used for the carriage of passengers where the characteristics of the vehicles do not conform to those of mainline railways. LRT systems employ steel wheel on steel-rail railway technology and have developed technically from the tramway. The light rail vehicles (LRVs) are lighter than normal railway or heavy rapid transit rolling stock and if adapted can run in the street, where legally in the United Kingdom they become tramcars. The dividing line between light rail and a tramway is indistinct but the term light rail has come to mean a new system with all the best features of a modernised tramway.

The DTp briefing note goes on to define tramway, tramroad, guideways (people movers) and guided buses as forms of light rapid transit. Other definitions (e.g. by the UITP Light Rail Commission[12]) emphasise the ability of light rail to be developed in stages from a modern tramway to a rapid transit system operating on its own right of way.

Selecting the System - Demand Considerations
The latter part of the 1980s and early 1990s have shown an upsurge of interest in light rail. This is due to increasing urban traffic congestion and its associated problems such as lower environmental quality and less viable city centres. However, before selecting a particular solution (eg heavy rail or light rail) it is essential that the transportation problems and future demands have been identified and assessed. For example, light rail, although extremely flexible in its application, may not be the most cost-effective solution to serve the problem being faced, although it may be preferred on grounds of image, joint development of an urban centre (such as pedestrianisation) or even sheer politics. The UK House of Commons Transport Committee[4] reporting on their examination of the light rail option concluded that:-

- light rail can be cost effective for a wide range of peak period usage;
- only heavy rail can serve the heaviest flows effectively;
- there is no clear population threshold for the viability of light rail although larger towns will offer most scope;
- light rail is an option for levels of demand in a wide band, between low flows best served by bus and very high flows best served by heavy rail.

There is considerable debate about the size of town or city that can justify urban rail systems. Evidence from Palmer[5] (see also Table 4.1), the French Ministry of Transport[7] and the evidence to the House of Commons Committee is that light rail can be cost effective with flows in the range 2,000 to 20,000 passengers per hour per direction whereas the equivalent flows for heavy rail lie in the range 10,000 to 50,000. The French suggest that above a capacity of 9,000 per hour or so, surface operation of light rail is difficult and segregation is essential, so this may be taken as an indicative cut-off point between heavy and light rail.

Outside London there are few cities in the UK where flows exceed 10,000 passengers per hour, hence much of the interest in light rail as a solution to providing car-competitive public transport. Evidence to the House of Commons Committee by the Chartered Institute of Transport indicates that light rail could be appropriate in towns of at least 200,000 population. In Germany public funds for capital investment in LRT is available for cities exceeding 300,000 population.

Population density and car ownership (see Tables 4.1 and 4.2 respectively) are both critical in determining the level of demand and hence the choice of system. The UITP found population densities in developed countries ranging from 3,824 persons per square kilometre in Manchester to only 1,245 (San Diego), but the densities in cities selected from developing countries were higher, at Tunis (6,975) and Tuen Mun (5,367)[13].

City and Travel Demand Classification

Size	Level I Small City	Level II Medium City	Level III Large City Conurbation	Level IV Metropolitan Conurbation
Population of service area	200-400,000	400-800,000	1,000,000	1,500,000
Population density in corridor (Inhabitants/mile^2)	5,000	9,000	14,000	20,000
Weekday patronage of a 12 mile-long corridor	20,000	40,000	80,000	120,000
Additional demand from feeder traffic	5,000	10,000	20,000	30,000
Passenger Miles per line mile	4,000	8,000	14,000	20,000

Table 4.1 Fields of Application of LRT Systems.

(Source: ref. 5)

39

	Cars per 1,000 Population	% of Public Transport
Calgary	792	17
Portland	685	6
San Diego	578	11
Sacremento	565	2
Nantes	433	23
Manchester	332	57
Tunis	52	52
Tuen Mun	36	9

Table 4.2 Relationship Between Car Ownership and Public Transport Mode Share. (source: ref. 14)

As one would expect there is a clear correlation between the level of car ownership and modal split and therefore one would expect light rail to be a more appropriate choice than heavy rail in cities where there is unlikely to be sufficient demand to justify heavy rail.

Besides population density and car ownership, another key consideration affecting demand in a rail corridor will be the level of integration with other modes such as bus feeders or park and ride. Whilst in Nantes 27% of light rail users access the light rail stops by bus and 5% park and ride, park and ride is typically more important in the new North American light rail systems. For example, seven stops in the Sacramento system have a combined total of 4,000 parking spaces; San Diego's system also has 4,000 spaces at 20 of its stops. Integration with other modes can therefore extend the catchment areas and raise the level of demand (see chapter 5).

The number of stations required also influences the system chosen, since heavy rail trains tend to have poorer acceleration (especially if diesel-powered), and require greater station facilities, but White[15] has suggested a method for estimating the optimum inter-station spacing. Good practice tends, however, to limit the number of stops on a line to around ten between the Central area and the end of the line, since passengers perceive the service to be slow with more stops than this. The number of boarders and alighters per stop also gives an indication as to a sensible number of stops, since there are costs involved in stopping (brake wear and tear, and also disbenefits to through passengers); a trade-off has to be made between these costs and providing a good service frequency. Large numbers of boarders and alighters (e.g. 50+) suggests an underprovision of service, whilst single-figure numbers may indicate the reverse; policy decisions to maintain regular service patterns or minimum frequency levels may, however, result in the latter occurring. It should also be remembered that choices between different service frequencies have implications in terms of costs and the number of drivers required, whilst varying train length can be used to offset frequency deficiencies if capacity (either in terms of signalling or number of available staff) is stretched. Such choices will also influence the personnel strategy for the system, as more frequent services may suggest that conventional traincrew and station barrier staff are preferable to more automated train operation and roving inspectors.

Other Modes - Competition or Integration?
Besides the decision to choose light rail or heavy rail it is necessary to consider the other transport modes (principally car and bus) and how they will impact on the decision.

In the United Kingdom, the Tyne & Wear Metro represents a classic example of a light rail system which when introduced was part of an overall integrated transport policy with bus routes organised to key interchange points (eg Gateshead, Four Lane Ends, Heworth), park and ride and an integrated ticketing policy allowing easy transfer between bus and rail. Following the 1985 Transport Act and the deregulation of buses, the level of integration between Metro and bus was reduced with many of the local bus operators choosing to compete with the metro by providing direct bus services to Newcastle-upon-Tyne city centre rather than via the purpose built interchanges. At the height of the integrated network the Metro system carried some 60 million passengers annually; the levels of patronage post deregulation with the competing bus network are some 50 million passengers annually.

When Nantes light rail system was introduced the bus services were re-organised to compliment rather than compete with the new system. The result is that not only has the overall volume of patronage on the public transport increased but the volume of bus passengers (see Table 4.3).

	1984 Without LRT (millions)	1986 With LRT (millions)	
Bus	51.1	53.0	
Tram	-	11.9	
Total	51.1	64.9	+ 27%

Table 4.3. Patronage of Public Transport in Nantes. (Source: ref. 8)

Sacremento in California represents a good example of a medium sized city where the introduction of light rail has enabled bus services to be re-organised; figure 4.1 illustrates how buses feed the LRT line (ref. 8).

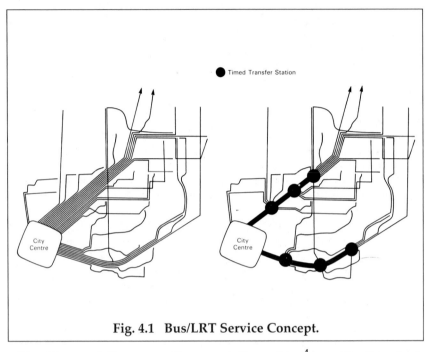

● Timed Transfer Station

City Centre

City Centre

Fig. 4.1 Bus/LRT Service Concept.

The House of Commons Transport Committee[4] specifically asked: "How does it (light rail) fit in with other modes, and what can it do that bus and heavy rail cannot?"

The Committee reported that many witnesses felt strongly that LRT should be developed as part of an integrated approach to transport planning particularly in relation to interchange, park and ride and ticketing. The Committee were encouraged that some co-ordination could be achieved in Tyne & Wear where deregulated bus services are competing.

Specific conclusions by the Committee on competing modes were as follows:-

i) **Heavy rail** - there may be benefits for light rail to replace parts of the suburban rail network. LRT may be a candidate for running a high frequency rapid transit service rather than a heavy low frequency service. The Committee recommended that the Department of Transport and British Rail investigate the conditions under which suburban rail services could be converted to light rail, including the possible transfer of ownership.

It should also be noted that it is relatively easy to provide interchange between light and heavy rail. Good examples include Meadowhall on the Sheffield Supertram system (see Fig. 4.2) and Stratford in East London (see Fig. 4.3).

ii) **Bus** - the bus operator's reaction in a deregulated environment is uncertain but there is a belief that although there will be some competition by offering improved limited-stop bus journeys along the LRT route, this will not occur where LRT has a strong advantage, for example in heavily congested areas where it has a segregated right of way. Complementary feeder buses to bus-rail interchanges are also likely. Many systems in France (e.g. Grenoble - see Fig. 4.4) and Germany have examples of bus feeder: light rail interchange (see Fig. 4.5).

iii) **Car** - the affect on private car traffic is difficult to assess although the Tyne & Wear Metro succeeded in attracting 8% of its passengers from former car users[11]. Recent unpublished work carried out by Harris Research for Sheffield Supertram gives some insight into how car users might react. The perception of light rail against the competing modes of bus and car were specifically researched. The conclusions were that Supertram as a concept was rated very highly and would be car competitive particularly for trips to the City Centre. Amongst those switching modes about a quarter of ridership would come from car and the remainder from bus. Supertram was perceived as a car minus rather than a bus plus.

To Segregate or not to Segregate?
Light rail systems differ from heavy rail systems because of their different construction standards. Light rail can be built with much sharper curves and steeper gradients than heavy rail (see chapter 14). They can be run as totally segregated systems like an ordinary railway (eg Tyne & Wear Metro) or as "tramways" sharing the road with other traffic or a mixture of the two (eg Manchester Metrolink). Segregation has been preferred in the past on safety grounds (although it can add to the cost), but this is changing as automatic control systems are being introduced which would prevent accidents with mainline trains, which may have different buffer heights as well as being substantially heavier.

43

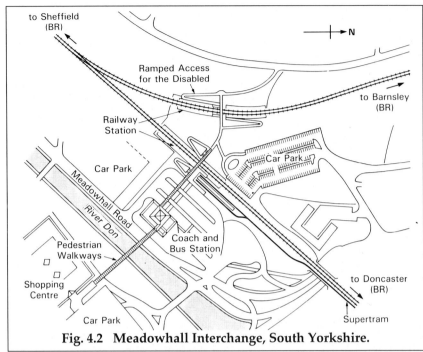

to Sheffield
(BR)

N

Ramped Access
for the Disabled

to Barnsley
(BR)

Railway
Station

Car Park

Car Park

Meadowhall Road

River Don

Pedestrian
Walkways

Shopping
Centre

Coach and
Bus Station

to Doncaster
(BR)

Car Park

Supertram

Fig. 4.2   Meadowhall Interchange, South Yorkshire.

Fig. 4.3   Stratford Rail Interchange, London.

44

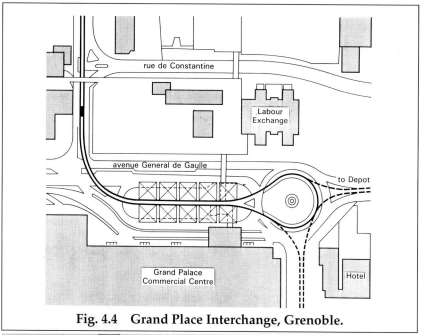

Fig. 4.4   Grand Place Interchange, Grenoble.

Fig. 4.5   Bus: Rail Interchange at Donnersberger Brucke, Munchen.

The flexibility of light rail is one of its major advantages over heavy rail. To underline this the UK Department of Transport have classified light rail into the following types, where the figures in brackets are the percentages of 18 of the 26 currently-promoted LRT schemes within the UK:

LRT1 - In roadway, shared with other traffic (22)
LRT2 - In roadway, track not shared except in emergency (11);
LRT3 - Track segregated from other traffic
a) driving on sight (51);
b) signal controlled (16).

The level of segregation ultimately adopted in any light rail scheme will depend on a variety of factors. However, full segregation can only be achieved by expensive tunnelling or other structures and generally a compromise needs to be reached between "affordability" and the advantages of full segregation. As much segregation as possible should be aimed for even with surface lines (ie. aim for LRT3 or LRT2).

There are many who argue that street running coupled with pedestrianisation enhances City Centre environments in a way that underground systems cannot (eg Zurich, Grenoble). Thessaloniki in Greece is considering the introduction of LRT[14] and studies there looked at four alternatives ranging from a 13.2 km system completely on the surface through to systems with up to 36% in underground sections. The conclusions were to recommend the surface option since:-

i) the difference in average commercial speed was only 5 minutes for the average trip length (19 km/hour for the surface compared to 25 km/hour for the maximum tunnel option);
ii) it has the lowest construction cost;
iii) it produced the highest economic return;
iv) it has the least impacts during the construction period;
v) it offers the possibility of improving the urban landscape quality by reducing the serious environmental impacts of traffic along its route.

Costs of LRT
Capital: The 1991 UITP Study[13] compared capital costs of a number of systems classifying them by type; at 1990 prices these ranged from £1.2m per km for the Toronto Harbourfront line to £13.5m per km for Grenoble lines 1 and 2. By comparison heavy rail lines and VAL type systems (automated) costs £30.8m per km in Lille to £36.4m per km in

Marseilles. A PTEG survey in conjunction with the DTI and Rail Industries Association[6] which analyses 18 schemes in the UK at various stages of preparation gives project costs ranging from £1.47m per km to £12.74m per km; the average is £4.7m per km. Although averages are heavily influenced by the opportunities for surface construction, chapter 17 (especially Table 17.3) gives some guidance on costing.

Comparative costs between the LRT systems in Nantes and Grenoble with the Lille VAL system and conventional heavy metro in Marseilles are shown in Table 4.4. It will be seen that the major savings in light rail are due to the much lower civil engineering, power supply costs. Consequently compared to heavy rail, light rail costs are characterised by a higher proportion of costs being incurred on the rolling stock. However, an initial estimate of capital costs versus the likely demand may be sufficient to indicate whether LRT is a realistic option, as in Honolulu[9].

Operating: Operating cost comparisons between light rail and heavy rail within the UK are limited to the Tyne & Wear Metro. The evidence[11] shows that light rail is more cost effective particularly when measured as a cost per passenger kilometre. Metro produced a net saving in operating cost and increased the number of passengers eightfold.

Technical Characteristics - Power Supply Considerations

As mentioned in previous sections light rail is very flexible and can be aligned at ground level, elevated or in tunnel. It can also cope with steep gradients; a maximum of an 8% gradient is permitted in the UK[3]. Where light rail tracks cross roads or footpaths the level of protection for other road users will depend on the classification (LRT1, LRT2, etc).

The light rail schemes which involve on-street sections require overhead supplies and are adopting as their standard 750v DC the maximum permitted. Totally segregated systems can use third rail (eg London Docklands) and/or higher voltages (eg Tyne & Wear 1500v DC)[2]. The electricity supply system of sub-stations (usually about every 3 to 4 km), feeder cables and earth returns are required along with the overhead wires suspended over the track for the vehicles to obtain their supply.

The overall capacity of the installed power supply system will be a function of the alignment, the number of LRVs in service and the LRV performance specification (typically LRV's are specified to give rapid acceleration and deceleration rates of 1.3 metres/s^2). Modern vehicles are controlled through the use of DC chopper or AC inverter

| | LIGHT RAIL | | | | | | VAL | | | HEAVY RAIL METRO | | |
| | Nantes | | | Grenoble | | | Lille[2] | | | Marseilles[3] | | |
	MFF	%	MFF PER KM	MFF	%	MFF PER KM	MFF	%	MFF PER KM	MFF	%	MFF PER KM
Land	20	3	2	65	7	7	36	*	1	120	2	7
Infrastructure (Civil Engineering)	165	26	16 }	466	47	52 }	4110	56	162 }	2730	52	154
Track	59	9	6 }			}			}			
Power Supply, Overhead Line Equipment	28	4	3	58	6	7 }	1808	25	71 }	1220	23	69
Buildings, Depot	66	10	6	157	16	18 }			}			
Rolling Stock	231	37	22	250	25	28	828	11	33	650	12	37
Design Fee/Project Management	61	10	6	100	10	11	518	7	20	480	9	27
TOTAL (MFF)	630		59	996		112	7300		287	5300		299
Other Improvement Works	304[1]			34								

MFF Million French Francs

Source: French Urban Public Transport Equipment 1988   * less than 0.5%

1. Includes consequential/miscellaneous work, environmental improvements
2. Line 1 and Line 1 bis   3. Lines 1 and 2

Table 4.4 French LRT Systems.

equipment. Regenerative braking can also be used which can produce up to 20% savings in energy consumption.

Conclusions
The chapter has shown the flexibility of LRT and that it can operate in a variety of situations (eg existing railway lines but not with heavy rail, on reserved rights of way, on street with other road vehicles or in pedestrianised streets). The key to the flexibility of LRT is its use of lightweight vehicles which can negotiate steeper gradients and sharper curves than heavy rail making it more cost effective to fit into the existing urban scene.

Only the very largest cities with flows in excess of 20,000 persons per hour per direction at peak times are likely to be able to justify new heavy rail lines. LRT therefore offers for many cities a public transport mode which can be car competitive by combining the speed and efficiency of rail with the accessibility required by customers.

References
1. Department of Transport (1991) "Light Rapid Transit Systems" - a briefing note by Public Transport Metropolitan Division of the DTp (March).
2. Hartland D J (1989) "Electric contact systems - overhead and low level" Proceedings of Light Rail '89 Conference, Bristol.
3. Her Majesty's Railway Inspectorate (HMRI) (1989) "Provisional Guidance Note on the Highway and Vehicle Engineering Aspect of Street-running Light Rapid Transit Systems" HMRI, London.
4. House of Commons Transport Committee Fourth Report (1991) "Urban Public Transport: Light Rail Option" HMSO, London.
5. Palmer, D. J. (1991) "Urban Public Transport - The Light Rail Option". CIT paper.
6. Passenger Transport Executive Group (1991) "Report on Light Rail Schemes in the UK", Strathclyde PTE.
7. Ministere des Transports (1988) "French Urban Public Transport Equipment", DTT and CETUR Paris.
8. Matoff, T. (1989) "Sacramento's Light Rail System - a Low-cost Application on a Low- density City", Proceedings of Light Rail '89 Conference, Bristol.
9. Schabas, M. (1988) "Quantitative Analysis of Rapid Transit Alignment Alternatives", *Transpn. Quaterly* 42 pp. 403-416.
10. Steer, J.K. (1991) "Socio-Economic Influences on the Role of Public Transport Modes in Major Urban Areas", *Transpn. Plng. Systs.* 1(3) pp. 3-12.
11. TRRL 1985 - "The Metro Report"
12. UITP International Light Rail Commission (1983).
13. UITP International Light Rail Commission (1991). "Financing Light Rail-Case Studies" 49th International Congress, Stockholm.

14. Vouglas, S. and Pitsavia - Latinapoulou, M. (1989) "Designing for on-street light rail in Thessaloniki, Greece" PTRC 18th Summer Annual Meeting - Proceedings of Seminar D.
15. White, P. (1986) "Public Transport: its Planning, Management and Operation" (2nd edn.) Hutchinson, 222pp. (pp. 102-104).

5. Design for passenger interchange

Ernest Godward

Introduction

A key element of planning passenger railways is the access to the system. The interchange between the railway and the rest of the world takes place through stations. It is very easy to plan on greenfield sites but planners have found it more difficult to replan for new operations around existing stations.

There are nine factors to be considered when designing a station. These are as follows:-

1). Provision of through tracks;
2). The station approach and departure tracks (the 'throat');
3). Platform tracks;
4). Design of rolling stock;
5). Station platforms and main circulating area;
6). Station management systems;
7). Station forecourts;
8). Post and parcel requirements; and
9). Other requirements including retail activities, air space
    developments and fire regulations.

Through tracks

Through tracks are useful for through trains which do not stop, for keeping freight trains and empty coaching stock movements out of the way and for locomotive run rounds. But these may not always be required, e.g. at terminal stations, major interchange stations and stations on lines with infrequent services. The minimum number of through tracks required can be determined from train timetables.

Station Approach and Departure Tracks

The approach and departure tracks can be simple for a station with one or two platforms on plain line. Even where the stations are off-line the approach and departure tracks will only require simple switches or points. The signalling may however be more complicated having to indicate to approaching trains which route is to be taken in order to regulate train speeds accordingly.

For major terminal stations and interchanges the approach and departure tracks will be relatively complicated. Ideally each platform should be capable of being reached from all tracks to allow flexibility of operation. In practice this was and is rarely possible. Studies in Japan show radically different station and track layouts to achieve this end.[14] Where stations have been modernised in many cases their approaches have undergone track remodelling to increase the flexibility of the layout and to permit parallel running. Recent examples of such exercises include London Kings Cross, Crewe, London Liverpool Street, Newcastle and York. Both Paris Nord and London Waterloo are currently being remodelled in connection with the Channel Tunnel international rail services.

Because of the complexity of the approaches to major stations the signalling control is inevitably more complex. When approaches are remodelled the renewal of signalling is advisable. For example when Liverpool Street was remodelled in 1989 a new Integrated Electronic Control Centre (IECC) was installed (see chapter 11). Initially this only controlled the station approaches. By stages this is being extended to cover all routes to Southend and Chelmsford. When things go wrong the ability to see the larger picture should enable line controllers to take effective action to minimise delays.

Platform tracks

The number of platform tracks required can be calculated from the number of trains to be handled and the length of time taken to load and unload trains. In the 1950's at London Liverpool Street it took an average of 20 minutes for an arrival and 30 minutes for a departure (see Table 5.1). Today, Intercity sector trains are allocated only 35 minutes in total. Due to late arrivals, many trains turn round much more quickly. The major changes since the 1950's have been electrification, elimination of all servicing except for minor cleaning (all major servicing is now

	1950 Arrivals	1950 Departures	1991 Arrival & Departure
Platform empty	5	5	5
Train into station	1.5	1.5	1.5
Passenger/parcels unload/load	9	17	24
Train out of station	1.5	1.5	1.5
Reserve time	3	5	3
TOTAL	20	30	35

Table 5.1 Comparison of Arrivals and Departures at Liverpool

done at the Norwich depot) and the operation of the train with a driving trailer removing the need for a locomotive change[4].

On suburban trains a turn-round can be achieved in 8 minutes for a train arriving empty at Liverpool Street whilst a train which is required to unload and load requires between 7 - 13 minutes[4].

Immediate access to a platform is most desirable, but in practice this is not always achieved. The number of platforms required is based on the peak hourly arrivals at a station. For example, if the peak arrivals rate is 32 trains and that turn-round can be achieved in 12 minutes (4 minutes for arrival and 8 minutes for departure), then:

Arrivals:-   32 x 4/60 = 2.133 (say 3 platforms).

This could handle 45 trains per hour.

Departures:-   32 x 8/60 = 4.266 (say 5 platforms).

This could handle 37.5 trains per hour.

Therefore the station platform capacity is 37.5 trains per hour on five platforms. This gives 17% spare capacity to handle late arriving or platform delayed trains.

Boardings, Alightings and Rolling Stock Design

It has become clear in recent years that the design of rolling stock is crucial to efficient station operation. The days of slam door stock are now limited as rolling stock is renewed and replaced with stock with sliding or plug leaf doors (which open outwards and then slide parallel to the side of the vehicle). In fact, this increases station stop times by increasing the average distance between seats and doors. Efficiency has had to make way for safety here as accidents involving passengers trying to jump onto moving trains have been numerous in the past.

Passengers need to be encouraged to stand away from doors. Passengers standing in train doorways reduce the rate at which passengers can board and alight (see Fig. 5.1). This problem can be overcome by the internal design of the stock. On LUL's heavily used Circle Line a redesign of the cars interiors, as part of a refurbishment project, led to a 16% increase in the circulating area of each car. The third objective of BR Network SouthEast sector's Networker project was a 15% increase in loading capacity[11]; Network South East are now having to remodel and redesign stations to handle the new stock.

Boardings and alightings can be speeded up by the use of sound warnings (usually called "hustlers" or "bruiters" in France). Such

53

sounds indicate that the doors will close within a few seconds. These have been used on modern rolling stock for some time and examples include the Thameslink and subsequent builds of stock. Platform announcements and military-style music may also help speed up boardings and alightings.

Fig. 5.1   Passengers boarding and alighting – London Victoria.

Station Platforms and main circulating areas

Platform width: Platforms must be able to accommodate a maximum length train. In the UK, the Railway Inspectorate will not now allow the use of platforms where only part of the train is platformed. BR are in the process of lengthening platforms to meet this requirement. Generally, InterCity platform lengths are 290 - 300 metres in length. This allows for a locomotive plus 13 carriages up to 20 metres long plus a safety margin of at least 8 metres. For longer coaches (e.g. Mark 3 and subsequent designs), formations are shorter, having a locomotive and 10 or 11 coaches. Such formations will probably include a Driving Van Trailer (DVT) (see Fig. 5.2) as many BR InterCity routes are now operated on a 'push-pull' basis, where the locomotive leads the train in one direction, but trails in the other, driving occurring from the DVT, with locomotive control by wires running the length of the train.

If passengers are evenly distributed along the platform, normal passenger density is around 1 passenger per square metre. As modern coaches may seat 64 passengers in standard class and be 20 metres long, the width of platform required can be calculated; here 3.2 metres is required. Extra width is required for any parcels trucks, "meeters" and "greeters" who may accompany travelling passengers, and to take account of bunching near platform entrances and exits.

When a train arrives, intending passengers tend to squash up to approximately three passengers per square metre leaving empty space on the platform. Alighting passengers can use the space created. If the train is fully seated and there are also standing passengers a certain amount of overload will occur on the platform, and station stop times may rise.

Calculation of such station stop times is also important as this will determine the capacity of a station. The latest BR Intercity 225 train consists of ten vehicles (eight coaches, a driving van trailer and a class 91 locomotive) in two types of formation. The standard formation has 480 seats plus 22 tip up seats. Assuming two doors per side per carriage, eight coaches per train, all seats occupied and no standing passengers,

Fig. 5.2   DVT at Birmingham New Street.

55

and five seconds per passenger per door, such a train with 502 passengers on board would be unloaded in 157 seconds. Thus:-

(502 * 5)/(8 * 2) = 157 seconds, which equates to 11511 passengers per hour.

Main Circulating Areas: Similar calculations to those above can be made in respect of walking speeds and space requirements. Tables 5.2 and 5.3 show three sets of design flows for circulating areas.

Different countries have adopted different design standards. The flow rates achieved will depend upon the level of congestion that there is at a station. Injured and invalided persons may require lifts or access ramps as might passengers travelling with children or luggage. Some stations will have ticket checks carried out at a barrier or an automatic ticket check gate; the planning capacity of LUL's UTS gates is around 24 passengers per minute. Flow rates need to be calculated in order to prevent congestion from building up to dangerous levels. Some metro systems now carefully monitor station flows to ensure safety of passengers. If flows become congested access to stations is closed off for a period of time.

Table 5.2. Design flows for station circulation areas.

	Hankin & Wright[10]	Department of Transport[5]
On level	88	66
Up stairs	62	) 46
Down stairs	69	)

Fruin[6] had a different approach, splitting areas into queuing areas, walkways and stairways and describing these areas under a number of flow conditions from free circulation to a complete breakdown in the flow of pedestrians. This was a more dynamic approach to a real dynamic problem.

In addition to providing appropriate circulation space the area outside of the platforms must generally contain the following:-

1). Ticket office and information counter (or ticket machines at smaller stations (see Fig. 5.3));
2). Waiting area for meeters, greeters and intending passengers. This area must contain information systems such as timetable boards or nowadays, more frequently, a solari indicator board, Dot Matrix

	QUEUING AREAS		WALKWAYS			STAIRWAYS		
	Pedestrian Density (m²/ped)	Ave. inter-person spacing (m)	Pedestrian Density (m²/ped)	Flow (Ped/m/min)	Ave. Speed (m/minute)	Pedestrian Density (m²/ped)	Flow (Ped/m/min)	Ave. Speed (m/minute)
Free Circulation	>1.21	>1.21	>3.25	<23.0	>74.8	>1.86	<16.4	>30.5
Uni-directional flows and free circulation. For reverse and cross flows with only minor conflicts.	1.21-0.93	1.21-1.07	3.25-3.30	23.0-32.8	74.8-75.4	1.86-1.40	16.4-23.0	30.5-32.2
Slightly restricted circulation due to difficulty in passing others. For reverse and cross flows with difficulty.	0.93-0.65	1.07-1.91	2.30-1.39	32.8-48.2	75.4-68.4	1.40-0.93	23.0-32.8	32.2-30.5
Restricted circulation for most pedestrians. Significant difficulty for reverse and cross flows.	0.65-0.28	0.91-0.61	1.39-0.93	49.2-65.6	68.4-61.0	0.93-0.65	32.8-42.6	30.5-27.7
Restricted circulation for all pedestrians. Intermittent stoppages and serious difficulties for reverse and cross flows.	0.28-0.19	<0.61	0.93-0.46	65.6-82.0	61.0-37.7	0.65-0.37	42.6-55.8	27.7-20.6
Complete breakdown in traffic flow with many stoppages.	<0.19	Close contact	<0.46	0-82.0	0-37.7	<0.37	0-55.8	0-20.6

Table 5.3 Planning for the Pedestrian in Queuing Areas, Walkways and Stairways. (Source 6)

Indicator (DMI) or TV style monitor showing information relating to arrivals, departures, punctuality and other essential matters;
3). Cafes, Restaurants and Bars;
4). Toilets;
5). Telephones;
6). Bookstall; and
7). Left luggage office or lockers.

As a rough guide, two metres square per person waiting is required to meet the above requirements but this will depend upon the location of the station, e.g. large city stations require large waiting areas, since passengers turn up longer in advance for longer distance services. Moreover, allowances need to be made for days when the peak loadings occur or when services are badly disrupted. In this situation trains will have to be turned round more quickly than timetabled.

Station Management Systems
A number of metro systems throughout the world are beginning to use computer based station management systems. London Underground[2]

Fig. 5.3 Simple ticket machine at Kirby Cross, Essex.

recently introduced one such system as a pilot trial at its Green Park station to assist station control and management. Safety, crowd control, crime prevention and engineering back-up are all part of a graphically-based system. Maps, schematics and CCTV of the station show where problems are occurring. The problems are assimilated from detectors and cameras situated throughout the station. The pilot scheme has cost £400,000 to implement.

Station Forecourts
These must have easy access for all vehicles and where possible public transport access should coincide with train arrivals and departures. If both trains and buses are frequent, then only a bus shelter may be required. In Germany and Holland many major rail stations also have major public transport interchanges. Examples such as Hamburg - Harburg and Hamburg - Barmbek are well documented examples[12]. In the UK the new interchange at Meadowhall will provide interchange between rail, light rail, bus, coach, taxi and car modes as well as providing for good pedestrian access (see chapter 4).

Where public transport interchange is made, timetable co-ordination can bring significant beneficial effects to both passenger and operators. Studies from the West Midlands showed between 9% and 17% generation as a result of integration of bus service timetables with the rail timetable[7].

Access by taxi tends to be by longer distance travellers. Space requirements for taxis should be determined by the loading and unloading times which averages out at two minutes. A short stay parking area (between 20 and 30 minutes duration) also needs to be provided. This will serve "kiss and ride" passengers (those being deposited by friends or relatives) as well as the "meeters" and "greeters". Public transport interchange, taxi ranks and short stay parking should be as close together as possible.

Long stay parking should be as close as possible but as the duration of parking is longer, passengers choosing to park their cars in such a facility may be willing to walk slightly further. Surveys of passengers using such modes of access to stations can determine the optimum provision for these items[8,15].

Park and Ride (p+r) provision are also important particularly in urban areas. Co-ordination of such facilities can help to reduce congestion on the approach to city centres. Studies in the 1980's in the West Midlands showed that where such facilities were put in they were used to capacity within about two years of opening[9,13,15]. The use of the facilities provided were considerably enhanced by the development of the system wide Travelcard ticket. One study suggested that the additional revenue benefits conferred on the public transport system covered the infrastructure costs of the car parks developed[1]. Where new links were created modelling suggested between 10% and 38% of new trips to rail could come from car users using p+r facilities[14].

Post and Parcel Requirements
Many railways throughout the world make use of such parcel and post facilities provided by passenger trains. In the UK, Red Star Parcel traffic provides station to station parcels using scheduled passenger trains. Customers are generally able to pick up parcels from offices in the station complex half an hour after arrival of the train on which the parcel has travelled. The service generally relies on delivery by the supplier to the station although in some larger cities collection for an additional fee can be arranged. The requirements for such systems are a set of secure offices with staff to deliver and collect parcels from trains at given times.

As well as providing a secure area on the station, secure facilities are required on the train. Mail therefore tends to travel with the Train Guard in a secured caged area. In the design of platforms provision must be made for bringing post to and from trains (possibly by ramp or conveyor) and sorting offices need to be in close proximity.

Retail Activities, Air Space Developments and Fire Regulations
Because stations are used by many people it became obvious to railway planners that some of the costs of stations might be offset by the revenues from retail and air space developments. In large cities railway stations are major focal points and it is logical that some users of the station might find certain retail activities of use. Apart from bookstalls, pharmacies, gift shops, florists, underwear, sock and shoe shops can now be found on station concourses. In 1990/91 British Rail derived £31 million in rent from enterprises trading at stations[3].

More importantly as stations have been modernised or redeveloped the opportunity to use the air space above the station has been taken. The Victorian builders of the railways created cathedral like structures in praise of their new creation - the railway. Modern day railway planners now allow developers rights to build office and shopping centres above the railway. In London in the last five years there have been five such schemes done by BR including Liverpool Street and Charing Cross. Across England, Wales and Scotland rent totalled £97 million in 1990/91.

Access requirements and fire regulations limit the amount of non railway activity that is permitted on railway station concourses. Moreover, Section 12 of the 1989 Sub-Surface Railways Act requires that any new underground or sub-surface railway station in the UK must be double-ended or at least have an emergency exit quite separate from the main entrance. In addition to increasing capital cost, this can affect retail opportunities as stations become classed as sub-surface if air rights are developed as at London Victoria.

Conclusions: There are, then, a large number of factors to be taken into account when planning passenger interchanges, and safety and legal requirements are much more rigorous for stations which are below ground. Whilst Victorian railway builders had a fairly free hand, modern systems are much more restricted by commercial and environmental pressures.

References
1. Anon (1984) "Car Parking at Rail Stations 1983", Unpublished report to the Operations Committee, West Midlands Passenger Transport Executive.
2. Anon (1991) "Tube Station Mission Control", *Modern Rlys.* pp. 33-34.
3. BR Annual Report and Accounts 1990/91.
4. British Railways (1989), Anglia Region Working Timetable. Section LA.
5. Department of Transport standard.
6. Fruin, J.J. (1971) "Pedestrian Planning and Design", Tables B1 - B3.
7. Godward, E. (1984) "Some Evidence on the Elasticity of Demand for Rail Services in the West Midlands", Public Transport Demand Elasticities Technical Seminar, Transport Studies Unit, University of Oxford.
8. Godward, E. (1987) "Return to Snow Hill", *Modern Rlys.* 44 pp. 533-538.
9. Godward, E. (1990) "Cross City Electrification", *Modern Rlys.* 47 pp. 643-647.
10. Hankin & Wright (1958) "Passenger Flows in Subways", *Opnl. Res. Quat.* 9 (2) pp. 81-88.
11. Marsden, C. J. (1991) "Towards Network 2000", *Rly. Mag.,* pp. 564-569.
12. Scott Hellewell, D. (1973) "Hamburg's Integration of Public Transport", *Traff. Engng. and Ctrl.* pp. 280-284.
13. Smith, G.C. (1984) "Park - and - Ride Modelling in the West Midlands Metropolitan County; An Assessment of LRT Operations", Unpublished MSc Dissertation, University of Birmingham.
14. Sone, S. (1990) "Squeezing Capacity out of Commuter Lines", *Developing Metros* 90, pp. 9-12.
15. West Midland County Council (Joint Transport Planning Unit) and MVA Consultancy (1984) "West Midland Rail Mode Choice Models".

6. Market Research for Passenger Railways

Rob Sheldon

Introduction
Market research is highly valued, and is well-used, by passenger railways, especially in Britain. British Rail have invested quite heavily, and are leading the way in innovative research techniques and approaches.

Research Usage
Research has typically been made use of for the following main purposes:

(1) **customer profiles (to obtain information on demand, market shares, market structure, customer activity)**
- on train passenger counts/station flow counts
- profile surveys/monitors (e.g. origin/destination, ticket held, fare paid, age, sex, etc)
- surveys of facility usage (e.g. on train catering, toilets, etc)
- general surveys of own/competitive mode usage

(2) **attitudinal research (to measure public/customer ratings of marketplace performance)**
- customer satisfaction rating surveys (e.g. for train punctuality, train comfort, catering standards, etc)
- image and awareness studies (e.g. of company, products offered, etc)

(3) **pricing research (to explore price sensitivities and tariff structure development within a competitive environment)**
- awareness studies (e.g. rail v competitive modes)
- appraisal of tariff structures through price elasticity examination (e.g. differentials 1st/Standard class, railcard discounts, etc)

(4) **design research (to assist in design and marketing processes)**
- for infrastructure development (e.g. new stations, rolling stock)

- input into redevelopment/refurbishment programmes
- product packaging and pricing

(5) **demand forecasting (to provide inputs to appraisal process)**
  - for product reformulation (e.g. changed ticket restrictions, revised tariff differentials)
  - infrastructure investment (e.g. new 'park and ride' stations, new rolling stock, new service/route, electrification)

(6) **advertising research (to help develop and test advertising campaign strategy development)**
  - copy development/testing
  - pre and post advertising awareness surveys

(7) **new product development (to assist in optimal new product development strategy)**
  - opportunity identification
  - concept development/testing
  - product and positioning specification
  - forecasting public response (e.g. awareness, attitudes, take-up).

Some areas are clearly more specialised than others with the more specialised purposes, as well as being less commonly pursued, typically also drawing upon more specialist suppliers and approaches.

Research Approaches
Passenger railway organisations make use of the broad range of research techniques available, embracing both qualitative and quantitative approaches.

Qualitative approaches essentially comprise either individual face-to-face in-depth interviews (reasonably unstructured in nature) or focus groups of up to eight or ten respondents (providing a more interactive forum for such in-depth discussion, guided by an experienced moderator). Such approaches are intended to provide a detailed, broad review of the issues involved rather than quantified responses that can be associated with statistical tests of robustness. The research location (on-train, at home, in offices, etc.) needs to be appropriate to the task in hand.

There are a variety of *quantitative* approaches available:

- simple passenger counts, perhaps using technological aids like video cameras

- self completion surveys (e.g. on train)
- postal surveys
- telephone interviews
- face-to-face interviews (e.g. at home, hall tests).

There are a number of broad issues which need to be covered when designing such research:

- is the approach suitable, given the complexity of the research issues involved ?
- are the right questions being asked?
- are they being asked in the right way?
- will the sampling approach avoid unplanned biases (e.g. can all potential respondents can be reached in this way, or will a high proportion of non-responses lead to potential bias?).

Very often qualitative research is used to help satisfy the researchers' concerns in regard to the first three questions. Sampling theory (see, for example reference 2) can assist with the fourth. As a further safety net, it is highly recommended that any approach be piloted sufficiently to help identify potential problem areas in advance of a commitment to be a major fieldwork programme.

The less expensive techniques are typically also the more restrictive, potentially leading to higher proportions of non-response (e.g. postal surveys) and a less "customised" approach (i.e. one less tailored to a specific respondent's circumstances). Judgement is needed to weigh up the advantages/disadvantages of alternative approaches.

Data collected in such surveys can be analysed using econometric techniques, whereby statistically-significant causal relationships can be derived from the results. Econometrics is beyond the scope of this text, and readers are referred elsewhere - to general texts[8], and also to railway-based specific examples[6,10]. Other modelling techniques may also be used[7,11]; the gravity model is sometimes used for the estimation of trip distribution[3].

There is one further stream of research used by the railways and not really covered by the above which is known in Europe as *stated preference* or *trade-off* research. Essentially this is a powerful specialist research approach which comprises both qualitative and quantitative research elements; it is discussed more fully below.

Increasing use is being made of computer-based interviewing techniques, not only with stated preference approaches. This trend has also been evident during the past few years in both telephone (CATI -

computer assisted telephone interviewing) and face-to-face (CAPI - computer assisted personal interviewing) quantitative approaches.

Different types of research tend to be appropriate for different market research purposes. Customer profile research tends to make predominant use of highly structured quantitative approaches whilst a mixture of qualitative and quantitative approaches will often feature in attitudinal, pricing, design and demand forecasting areas. Advertising research will typically make extensive use of qualitative approaches, these featuring quite heavily also in new product development work. Any use of stated preference research will tend to be restricted to pricing, demand forecasting, new product development and, perhaps to a lesser extent, design research.

Stated Preference (SP)

This research approach was introduced into Europe from the United States in the late 1970s. In the US it had tended to be mainly used for new product development work in non-service 'fast moving consumer good' sectors and marketed under a variety of different terms e.g. conjoint analysis, functional measurement. It contrasts with traditional techniques measuring actual behaviour (Revealed Preference (RP)) methods by investigating more hypothetical situations.

Essentially, it is a technique which enables the relative importance of product components to be examined in a quantified way, enabling more focused product rationalisation and development. It works by asking (potential) customers to evaluate a series of experimentally designed product options which are presented as alternative packages. Evaluation can be by way of a ranking of packages into the respondent's order of preference, by rating each or by making choices between two or more packages.

An important issue in the use of stated preference methods is the quality of the survey and the context in which the survey questions are asked. If useful results are to be obtained from stated preference methods, the survey needs to be of the highest possible quality and the context in which the stated preference questions are asked should be as realistic as possible. For this reason most practitioners have a strong preference for face-to-face interviews, conducted by experienced interviewers and also structured to ensure:

- that the background to the respondent's evaluation process (e.g. situational constraints, demographic characteristics, planning processes) is fully   understood by the researcher
- that the respondent is not "educated" about any misperceptions

he/she might currently hold about a particular product or service, say, or led by "enticing" stimuli (such as a new station photographed on a very sunny day) to react more (or less) positively to change than he/she might otherwise have done

-   that complete alternative specifications are provided, since individuals perceive concepts as a whole (that is, as products) rather than as the sum of a number of separate factors.

Typically, the information is provided to respondents by way of option cards or computer screens. For instance, a preference based approach might well require a respondent to appraise some eight or nine cards each comprising one option made up of differing levels of the variables being examined (see Fig. 6.1).

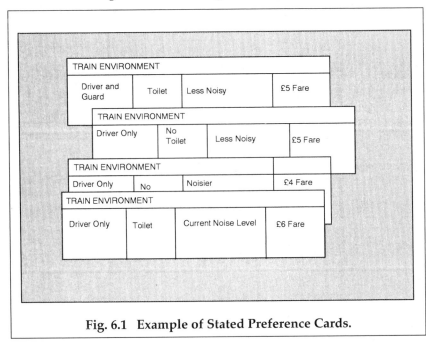

Fig. 6.1   Example of Stated Preference Cards.

Some of the information is normally preprinted on to the cards; other items may well need to be filled in by the interviewer in line with the experience of the respondent (related, for example, to the fare actually paid), providing a "customised" approach. In order to maximise the usefulness of the results (and therefore minimise time spent interviewing), initial questions may also be asked to isolate those thresholds (or boundary values) at which respondents are genuinely trading attributes off against each other.

From the chosen rankings, weighting coefficients can be derived e.g. a respondent's Value Of Time can be easily determined if they say they are willing to pay 50p to save 10 minutes. The probability of the respondent actually choosing an alternative can then be estimated by a logit model e.g.

$$P(a) = \exp(a) / (\exp(a) + \exp(b)),$$

where P(a) is the probability of choosing option a, and the terms exp(a) and exp(b) represent the exponential of the generalised cost functions chosen for the options (see also chapter 1). Further details of the method can be found in references 4 and 13.

Applications of SP: One of the first applications in Europe was a major study for British Rail which took over two years to complete. This research project[9] was concerned with defining demand elasticities for primary service characteristics of long distance rail travel - price, journey time, service frequency and interchange. RP approaches involving the development of econometric models from ticket sales data had proved to be unsuccessful in separately identifying values for **all** of these variables and such models were certainly unable to distinguish between distinct market segment groupings e.g. leisure cf business travel. However, the study proved to be enormously successful and was well received. The types of demand elasticity results that were produced are shown in Table 6.1.

Table 6.1   Rail Demand Elasticities by Journey Purpose.
(Source 9)

Purpose	Fare	Time	Frequency (trains/hr)
Business	-0.7	-0.7	+0.2
Optional	-1.4	-0.5	+0.2

Since then British Rail has invested heavily in the development of the technique using it predominantly to estimate further market segment-based elasticities, for input into feasibility appraisals (e.g. station investment), for product rationalisation (e.g. changed railcard discounts) and for new product development (e.g. the development of InterCity's Silver Standard product). Other operators and authorities have also used the technique[12,14].

Development of the technique has been quite dramatic with a major breakthrough emerging in the mid 1980s, with the development of approaches capable of more direct examination of consumer choice behaviour between competitor products. Previously such techniques had been used predominantly to look at preferences between specific product variations.

These recent developments have increased the attraction of the approach substantially, paving the way for an important new research avenue - the use of stated preference in the process of forecasting demand and market shares for potential LRT systems (e.g. Manchester and Birmingham). Typically, these projects have involved the calibration of hybrid revealed preference/stated preference forecasting models, where the two data sources are treated as complementary - the stated preference data providing information for areas for which no suitable revealed preference information is available.

The increased use being made of stated preference techniques in this context has led the Department of Transport to issue guidelines upon stated preference research practices for Section 56 funding purposes. (Section 56 provides a source of state capital investment funding for major transportation investment programmes).

More recent initiatives have involved exploring how such techniques could be developed to estimate the potential for generated demand (new business) rather than re-allocated demand (from one mode to another or one time period to another) which has been the focus to date. This stream of research known as "stated intentions" is still in a very early developmental stage.

Conclusions: Market research is used by railways for a large number of applications, including as a basic part of planning future developments. Both qualitative and quantitative methods are used; within the latter, there is a split between Revealed Preference and the developing technique of Stated Preference.

SP has a number of advantages over RP, being particularly useful for quantifying the effects of qualitative variables, and in new product situations where no RP data exists (e.g. for LRT systems (see chapter 4) and new stations (see chapter 7)). It can also be more data-efficient, as by asking a series of hypothetical questions, several observations per individual can be collected. It is also statistically-efficient; for example, surveys can be designed to avoid correlation. Moreover, it facilitates the examination of non-linearities; for instance, different levels of rail frequency might be specified separately, a technique sometimes known as piecewise estimation.

However, there are also potential problems[7,10], and customisation of the approach is required to avoid undue bias. Respondents' abilities to provide sensible answers limit how hypothetical situations can be whilst, when used for forecasting, a potential technical difficulty known as the scale factor problem[1,15] needs to be overcome. The references suggested below give further insights into this and other technical issues affecting SP.

References

1. Bates, J.J. (1988) "Econometric Issues in Stated Preference Analysis", *Jnl. of Transp. Econ. & Pol.* 22 pp. 56-69.
2. Birn, R., Hague, P., and Vangelder P., (1990) "A Handbook of Market Research Techniques".
3. Bruton, M.J. (1975) "Introduction to Transportation Planning", 2nd ed., Hutchinson, 251pp.
4. Davidson, P.W. (1989) "An Introduction to Stated Preference Techniques", PTRC Course "A Short Course on Stated Preference Techniques".
5. Fowkes, A.S. (1991) "Recent Developments in Stated Preference Techniques in Transportation Research", PTRC Summer Annual Meeting G pp. 251-263.
6. Goulcher, A. (1991) "Fares Elasticities for Underground Travel", PTRC Summer Annual Meeting G pp. 99-110.
7. Jessop, A. (1990) "Decision & Forecasting Models with Transport Applications", Ellis Horwood, 461pp.
8. Johnston, J. (1972) "Econometric Methods", McGraw-Hill, 437pp. (esp. chs 1&2).
9. Kroes, E., and Sheldon, R., (1988) "Stated Preference Methods: An Introduction".
10. Nash, C.A., Preston, J.M. & Hopkinson, P.G. (1990) "Applications of Stated Preference Analysis", Department of Transport Conference of Longer-Term Issues, July.
11. Ortuzar, J. de D. & Willumsen, L.G. (1990) "Modelling Transport", Wiley, 375pp.
12. Ray, B., Davidson, P.W. & Chard, B. (1991) "Developing a Realistic Public Transport Strategy for the City of Truro from Public Attitudes", PTRC Summer Annual Meeting H pp. 253-278.
13. SDG (1990) "Stated Preference Techniques: A Guide to Practice" (2nd ed).
14. Sheldon, R., Bottom, C., and Golob, T., (1986) "An Examination of the Priorities that Passengers Place upon Features of the London Underground System".
15. Wardman, M. (199) "Stated Preference and Travel Demand Forecasting: an

Examination of the Scale Factor Problem", Transpn. Res. 25A pp. 79-89.

16. Wardman, M. & Fowkes, A.S. (1991) "Investigating the Functional Form of the Demand Curve for Rail Passenger Transport", PTRC Summer Annual Meeting G pp. 111-121.

7. Estimating the Demand for New Lines and Stations

Jonathan Preston

INTRODUCTION

The opening of new passenger rail services and stations has recently become important. Two main issues have dominated research in this area. The first relates to forecasting, where British Rail (BR) have developed a detailed methodology for existing services; however, it is unsuitable for new services. The second relates to assessing the most appropriate forecasting approach. New stations and services are generally modest investments (except when underground) and, therefore, the appraisal methods deployed should reflect this.

In this chapter, aggregate approaches (including trip rate and direct demand models), based on zonal data, will be described first, followed by a range of disaggregate approaches (including methods based on revealed preferences and/or stated preferences), based on data at the individual level. Lastly, some conclusions will be drawn with respect to the choice of appraisal methodology and the policy implications of some of our findings. As this chapter will have a practical emphasis, some of the technical issues will only be outlined briefly, and the interested reader is referred elsewhere[11,12].

The Boom in New Stations and Services

Such has been the extent of the recent boom in passenger rail services that it is a non-trivial task to collate exact figures. Monitoring work carried out by the author and others (in particular ref. 16) indicates that over 200 new stations have been opened on publicly-owned passenger railways in Britain since 1970, with the vast majority on the Regional Railways' network. That this represents something of a policy U-turn is illustrated by Table 7.1. In addition, 15 new lines have been opened, although one (Kettering-Corby) has subsequently closed[4].

Table 7.1: Opening/Closure of Stations on Publicly-Owned Passenger Railways in Britain.
Includes Tyne and Wear Metro and Docklands Light Railway

	Open	Closed	Net Balance
1970-74	18	130	-112
1975-79	38	13	+25
1980-84	44	10	+34
1985-90	116	14	+102
TOTAL	216	167	+49

The main phase of openings began in the early 1980s. An important contributory factor was the 1981 (Speller) amendment to the 1962 Transport Act, which has facilitated the experimental opening of new stations and services that can subsequently be closed without undergoing the (expensive) normal procedures. There is some evidence that the 'boom' has slowed down, at least as far as conventional rail is concerned (although light rail may continue it), probably because the best sites have already been developed.

The 'Methodology Gap'

British Rail have developed a reasonably sophisticated approach to modelling the demand for existing services that has been given the acronym MOIRA[21]. This approach is largely based on a number of time-series studies that have developed elasticities with respect to fare, levels of service quality and GNP (see, for instance, ref. 8).

However, such an approach is inapplicable to the case of new rail stations and services for at least two, closely-related, reasons. First, elasticity models are only applicable for small changes, but the introduction of a new rail service is clearly non-marginal. Secondly, elasticity models are applied multiplicatively to a base level of demand. A problem here is that for local rail services, assuming a reasonably fine zoning system, zones with no nearby rail station can have zero base demand.

However, for local rail services, particularly those operated by Regional Railways, there has been something of a 'methodology gap'. Fortunately, a number of different techniques have been developed; these tend to be cross-sectional rather than time-series based i.e. they examine a group of observations at a single period of time, rather than a single observation over a number of time periods. These modelling approaches may be classified in terms of two dimensions, the first of which is related to the specification of the decision unit. The distinction is normally between aggregate aproaches based on zonal data (for example based on the definition of a station's catchment area(s)) and disaggregate approaches (usually based on data at the level of the individual. The second distinction is related to the type of behaviour being measured. Here the distinction is between the Revealed Preference (RP) approaches, based on observed behaviour, and Stated Preference (SP) approaches, based on hypothetical behaviour (see Chapter 6).

The Scale of Investment
A number of different types of new stations have been opened in Britain in the recent past. The vast majority serve residential areas and are largely unmanned (at least outside the Network SouthEast area). There have also been a number of stations that attract, rather than generate travel. These may serve factories, offices and education establishments, with the Cross City Line in Birmingham providing good examples with Longbridge, Five Ways and University stations respectively. Other stations may provide better access to central business areas (eg Argyle Street in Glasgow), out-of-town shopping centres (eg Gateshead Metro Centre, Meadowhall) and airports (eg Stansted). These stations will require their own specialised forecasting approaches, although for small-scale developments estimating rail trips as a function of either proposed employment levels or retail floorspace may suffice. Similarly new stations on the InterCity network such as Birmingham International or Bristol Parkway require their own forecasting methodology (Parkway stations are out-of-town stations with ample parking provision, specifically aimed at the park-and-ride market).

The design of unmanned halts serving residential areas is relatively basic and hence costs are correspondingly low. The typical capital costs of new stations in West Yorkshire, based on two wooden platforms capable of accommodating four car trains, simple shelters, access ramps and lighting were around £100,000 in the early 1980s. Indeed these low costs were an impetus to the new station boom, although the costs of station construction have subsequently increased in real terms. Operating costs of maintaining and administering a new station were notionally estimated at £1,700. This ignores the additional fuel and braking costs of stopping a train which, for an hourly service, may come to an additional £1,700 p.a. or so[18]. The key assumption is that the additional stop can be accommodated without any additional resources in terms of rolling stock and staff i.e. that there is some slack in the timetable.

If this assumption holds then Table 7.2 shows that fairly low levels of demand will be sufficient to justify a new station financially (for derivation, see refs. 9 & 15). For example, a single-platform rural station with capital costs of £60k (mid 1984 prices) and a mean single fare of £1, may only require 25 ons and offs per day (30 per day, including braking and fuel). Using trip rates developed in West Yorkshire (see section 8.2.1), the demand of 25 ons and offs was estimated to require a population within 800 metres of only around 800. By contrast, a double-platform inner city site, with a difficult location and hence capital costs of £150k and a mean fare of only 30 pence will require demand of 177 ons and offs per day (196 if braking and fuel costs are included).

Table 7.2: Demand and Catchment Area Population Required for a New Station to Break-Even (Mid 1984 Prices).

Mean Fare (pence)	New Station Costs	Daily Ons and Offs	Population within 800m
	A	81	2550
30	B	125	3900
	C	177	5550
	A	41	1300
60	B	63	1950
	C	89	2800
	A	25	800
100	B	38	1200
	C	54	1700

A Capital Costs £60k, Recurrent Costs £1.5k pa
B Capital Costs £100k, Recurrent Costs £1.7k pa
C Capital Costs £150k, Recurrent Costs £1.7k pa

The above calculations assume that the additional stop does not deter existing travellers. The argument for this assumption is that passengers are unable to perceive time penalties as small as one or two minutes. However, when a number of new stations are being considered on the same line this assumption is unrealistic. There are likely to be some existing passengers at the margin who will be put off rail travel. This factor is likely to count particularly against inner city sites where the trains are generally already well loaded.

On their own new stations are relatively modest investments but it may be useful to consider three scales of expenditure:

(i) The one-off unmanned halt on an existing rail service with capital costs under £0.5 million (in many cases substantially so).

(ii) Packages of unmanned halts or an individual manned local station on existing rail services. The costs here may be in the range £0.5M to £10M (usually £2-£3M).

(iii) New stations on a new service. The costs may include upgrading a freight only rail line to passenger services, new rolling stock and in some cases new sections of track. The cost may range from £0.75M (the Walsall-Hednesford line) to over £12M (the Leicester - Burton (Ivanhoe) line). For example, about £7M was spent on redeveloping the link between Birmingham Snow Hill and Moor Street (see Fig. 7.1), but such costs are still well below the costs of most Light Rapid Transit schemes (for example, the first phase of the Manchester Metrolink is £90 million).

£5 million is an important threshold because schemes with capital costs in excess of this are eligible for grants from central government under section 56 of the 1968 Transport Act. However, any application for grant requires a detailed assessment study to be undertaken that examines a range of options and considers non-user benefits (such as congestion relief, environmental improvements and developmental

Fig. 7.1 New Station: Birmingham Moor Street.

effects) as well as revenue and user benefits (see ref. 7). This in turn requires a detailed forecasting methodology.

AGGREGATE METHODS

Two main aggregate methods have been used. These are trip rate models (which tend to express rail travel solely as a function of population characteristics of the origin catchment area), and direct demand methods (which also take into account the attractiveness of destinations and level of service characteristics of rail and competing modes).

Trip Rate Models

Surveys in West Yorkshire[10] identified two main station catchment areas: the 0-800m zone, accounting for 62% of users and the 800m-2km zone, accounting for 25% of users. Given information on actual usage simple trip rates can be easily developed as shown by Table 7.3. This table gives data for the first nine stations opened in West Yorkshire and two opened in the East Midlands. Overall, it is estimated that an average of around 29 rail trips per day per thousand population are made by people living within 800m of a station and 4 trips per day per thousand population by people living between 800m and 2km from a

Table 7.3: Trip Rates for 11 New Stations (Daily ons and offs per thousand population - rounded).

	0-800m	800m-2km	% from beyond 2km
Fitzwilliam	17	0	20
Deighton	14	2	8
Crossflatts	20	6	20
Slaithwaite	24	6	21
Bramley	15	3	9
Saltaire	31	8	9
East Garforth	102	10	1
Frizinghall	29	1	3
Sandal & Agbrigg	11	4	23
Langley Mill	10	3	43
South Wigston	30	2	21
Unweighted Mean	27.5	4.1	16.2
Standard Deviation	24.6	2.9	11.3

station. A further 16% of trips are made by people livng beyond 2km (Note, however, that these figures refer to new stations only one or two years after opening and as a result may be underestimates).

The standard deviations indicate that there are large variations in trip rates. The highest trip rates for people living within 800m is recorded at East Garforth, which is perhaps prime commuter belt, and the lowest trip rates are either for sites close to central areas (Sandal, Deighton, Bramley) or for free-standing, industrial towns (Langley Mill). The other main source of variation is the percentage of trips coming from beyond 2km. For stations close to a main centre, this figure will be between 0 and 10%. For stations on the edge of the built up area a more typical figure will be 20%. For the one free-standing town in our sample the figure is over 40%, reflecting the greater proportionate use of this station for long distance travel.

Direct Demand Models

The main problem with the trip rate models presented in Table 3 is that they are too simplistic. In particular, they fail to take into account the socio-economic composition of the origin population, the relative attractiveness of destinations or the levels of service of rail and competing modes (e.g. road congestion). These features can be incorporated into a 'trip end' model, as developed for Greater Manchester PTE[1]; however, such a trip rate model only tells us how many people per day use a station but not where they are going to, which is vital for revenue estimation. An approach that attempts to get round this is the direct demand (or aggregate simultaneous) model approach which forecasts the flow of rail traffic between station pairs. This type of model has been developed for new stations in West Yorkshire[11], and has subsequently been applied to over 70 sites in 12 different counties. The main findings of this approach have been that:

(i)   Rail usage is strongly positively correlated with the proportion of the population in social classes I and II (Professional and Managerial) and weakly, positively correlated with social class IIIN (skilled non-manual).

(ii) Rail usage is moderately negatively correlated with the proportion of the population in social class IIIM (skilled manual) and V (unskilled).

(iii) Rail level-of-service variables have very strong influences, particularly fare and frequency. However, these results are affected by the simultaneity problem (are high levels of service caused by high levels of demand or is it vice-versa?). Expressing rail's level of service as a generalised cost may be a pragmatic way of reducing this problem.

(iv) The level of service of competing modes (in particular bus frequency and car speed) also has an effect. Again it may be better to incorporate the generalised cost of bus and car, but it is often difficult to obtain statistically significant parameter estimates. In part, this is because aggregate methods cannot pick up the effect of out-of-vehicle time as this varies as much within zones as between them. Here, disaggregate methods are more helpful.

Direct demand models are affected by a number of statistical problems in addition to simultaneity and lack of variation in key variables as mentioned above. Other problems include multi-collinearity (correlation between variables such as car and rail journey time) and heteroscedasticity (non constant variance of the error term). As a result the amount of variation these models explain, as measured by R^2, is often little more than half, although a high R^2 does not necessarily indicate a good model. Nonetheless, a model developed in West Yorkshire has proved to be reasonably accurate in specific circumstances. Initially, the model overestimated the demand at the first six new stations in the county but demand has grown over time so the the model has become more accurate. Additional time-series work estimated that the 'product take-off curve' for new stations might span five years, be linear and relatively steep (demand in year one only being around 57% of that in year five).[10]

DISAGGREGATE METHODS

The amount of walk and wait time that is incurred in using public transport is one of the crucial determinants in choosing that mode. This can only be accurately measured on an individual basis and hence two groups of disaggregate approaches have been widely used for estimating public transport demand; these are discussed in turn below.

Revealed Preference (RP) Methods

These methods are based on observed behaviour and should be used where stations and services exist that correspond to those new stations and services being proposed. A recent example of such a model is one developed in order to predict the demand for a new rail service to the the towns of Brighouse and Elland in West Yorkshire[19]. This was done by calibrating a model based on the travel behaviour of individuals living in the near-by towns of Mirfield and Sowerby Bridge and then applying this model to times and cost data collected in the Brighouse-

Elland area (see Table 7.4). However, the model is a hierarchical logit one because there is strong evidence both here and in earlier work [10,11] that bus and train should not be treated as independent alternatives.

The Brighouse-Elland model was calibrated by a three-stage bottom-up approach. The first stage (the lowest nest) involved predicting the choice of access mode, given rail as the chosen main mode. The alternatives considered were walk, bus, park-and-ride and kiss-and-ride (with the latter being the base). The second stage (the middle nest) predicts the choice between bus and rail, given that public transport is the chosen main mode. The information from the lower nest is incorporated by the logsum variable, the parameter value of which should always be greater than 0 and less than or equal to 1. The third stage involves the choice of main mode, with the information from the middle and lower nest again being incorporated by a logsum variable, the parameter value of which should again be between 0 and 1, but should also be less than the value of the previous logsum parameter.

The data supported the hierarchical structure but also illustrates a number of problems with RP models. Although over 1100 interviews were undertaken, only a small number of observations (280) were used in the calibration stage, which reflects the data inefficiency of RP methods (see chapter 6). Partly as a result of the low number of observations, a large number of the parameter values were insignificant at the 5% level (9 out of 17), whilst there was some indication of correlation between time and cost variables. Overall goodness of fit was modest (although a good fit, as measured by rho-squared, is between 0.2 and 0.4). This all reflects the statistical inefficiency of RP methods.

Stated Preference (SP) Methods
SP methods are often preferred for two reasons. First, RP methods may be impossible because a comparable local rail service does not exist.

This was believed to be the case in two major studies undertaken in the East Midlands examining the case for new rail services between Leicester and Burton-on-Trent (the Ivanhoe line) and between Nottingham and Worksop, via Mansfield (the Robin Hood line). Secondly, SP has a number of advantages over RP, as we have already seen in chapter 6.

An example of the type of model that has been developed with SP data is given by Table 7.5. This model was used to forecast the demand for a new rail service to Clitheroe in Lancashire [13.] Like most SP models it is based on a simple binary logit. The table shows that models can be developed based on very small numbers of individuals (only 29 in the case of the bus v train model), although one would normally aim for

Table 7.4: Model Results for an RP Model to Predict Rail Demand in Brighouse and Elland.

(A) Lower Nest - Choice of Access Mode for Rail

	Parameter value	t-statistic	Adjusted value
ASC - Walk	1.355	1.55	2.302
ASC - Bus	0.441	0.59	0.035
ASC - Park'n'Ride	1.274	1.44	0.329
OVT	-0.177	3.18	V of OVT5.36 p/min
IVT	-0.043	0.62	V of IVT1.30 p/min
Cost	-0.033	1.80	

Rho-squared 0.04, Percent Correct 67, Observations 74.

(B) Middle Nest - Choice of Public Transport Mode

	Parameter value	t-statistic	Adjusted value
ASC - Rail	0.915	2.07	-0.384
Walk	-0.034	1.09	V of Walk 2.13 p/min
Wait - Rail	-0.074	1.71	V of Wait 4.63 p/min
IVT	-0.043	2.83	V of IVT 2.69p/min
Cost	-0.016	2.32	
Logsum	0.926	4.17	

Rho-squared 0.28, Percent Correct 67, Observations 147.

(C) Upper Nest Choice of Mode

	Parameter value	t-statistic	Adjusted value
ASC - Car Driver	1.283	2.63	1.664
ASC - Car Passenger	0.339	0.73	0.318
IVT	-0.021	1.54	V of IVT 2.33 p/min
Cost	-0.009	3.64	
Logsum	0.266	2.23	

Rho-squared 0.17, Percent Correct 60, Observations 158.

Abbreviations: ASC = Alternative Specific Constant; IVT = In-Vehicle Time; OVT = Out-of-Vehicle Time (Walk and Wait Time) substantially larger sample sizes. Nonetheless, the t-statistics and rho-squared measures suggest a relatively good fit.

Table 7.5: Stated Preference Models Developed to Predict the Demand for a New Rail Service to Clitheroe.

(A) Bus v Train Model (t-statistics in brackets)

	Parameter Value		Value in Pence	
ASC - Bus	-0.732	(1.63)	-22.73	(1.58)
Bus Headway	-0.018	(1.76)	0.55	(1.93)
Total Time	-0.072	(5.79)	2.25	(5.36)
ASDV - Work/Education	1.063	(3.56)	33.00	(3.13)
Cost	-0.032	(8.95)		

Rho-squared 0.55, Percent Correct 81, Observations 507, Individuals 29.

(B) Car v Train Model (t-statistics in brackets)

ASC - Car	1.008	(2.85)	61.07	(2.09)
FREQ30	0.366	(1.55)	22.19	(1.44)
FREQ20	0.874	(3.24)	52.94	(2.85)
FREQ15	0.961	(3.69)	58.22	(2.82)
Ln (Walk)	-1.323	(5.70)		
Ln (IVT)	-1.918	(7.16)		
Cost	-0.017	(6.29)		

Rho-squared 0.32, Percent Correct 70, Observations 892, Individuals 56.

Abbreviations:
ASDV = Alternative Specific Dummy Variable
FREQ30, 20, 15 = Rail frequency every 30, 20 and 15 minutes.

However, SP methods are not without their own problems, and the development of hybrid preference models that incorporate both RP and SP approaches is also worth considering, as is combining aggregate and disaggregate approaches in an attempt to incorporate trip generation as well as mode choice.

The conventional application of SP models (e.g. as in the Walsall-Hednesford rail study[5]) is to apply them with information on the origin/destination of existing trips and aggregate engineering times and costs. A number of problems emerge here. The use of a disaggregate model with aggregate data will lead to biases, whilst the engineering times and costs will be greatly affected by measurement error. Moreover, in many areas detailed information on current travel by car and bus does not exist and is very expensive to collect. An alternative is to carry out a self-completion survey of the area where a new service is to be introduced in order to collect information on existing travel patterns as well as allowing respondents to state their intention of using the new service[3]. However, due to a combination of systematic biases, these stated intentions forecasts may be taken to be gross overestimates. Checks on the extent of these biases can be supplied by validation with census information and by carrying out an SP survey. Based on four major case studies, it is estimated that stated intentions forecasts overestimate rail usage by an average of 60%, even if it is assumed that nonrespondents to the survey are nonusers. Car users are particularly likely to overstate their demand. This stated intentions/preference approach requires validation, but it can provide reasonably accurate forecasts if applied carefully.

Policy Implications
Given Britain's rapidly changing demography, there will always be the case for some new stations and services (and indeed, in some instances, closures). However, policy implications require careful consideration and depend crucially on the objectives of the sponsoring authority. Decisions should not be made on patronage or indeed gross revenue alone. This is illustrated by Table 7.6, where it can be seen that the rankings of six new stations in West Yorkshire vary greatly depending on the criteria being used. Particularly important issues are whether the sponsoring authority is a dominantly-commercial body (and if so whether it is responsible just for rail or an integrated public transport network), or whether its main aim is to maximise social surplus. In terms of relative priorities, very different policies can emerge, whilst in terms of absolute priorities, social cost-benefit analysis tends to be most favourable to new rail schemes, although in some cases restricted financial appraisal may give favourable results.

Table 7.6: Ranking of Six New Stations in West Yorkshire based on Various Criteria.

	Demand	Gross Revenue	Financial Appraisal -Rail only	Financial Appraisal -Rail and Bus	Social Cost-Benefit Analysis
Fitzwilliam	6	5	5	3	1
Deighton	5	4	4	2	2
Crossflatts	4	1	2	1	4
Slaithwaite	3	6	6	4	3
Bramley	2	3	1	6	6
Saltaire	1	2	3	5	5

Source: ref. 10.

CONCLUSIONS

Choice of Appropriate Forecasting Method

The accuracy of aggregate and disaggregate RP methods has been compared in detail in ref. 1, whilst the accuracy of SP methods has still to be proven. The conventional approach, as applied to the Walsall-Hednesford line, appeared to underestimate demand, but the reasons are not clear, although it may be that generated travel was underestimated[5]. The Stated Intentions/SP forecasts that have been produced for a number of lines have yet to be validated but Table 7.7 shows that they are broadly consistent with trip rates for new lines that have opened. Another useful check is to examine the elasticities and values of time implied by models, which is done in Table 7.8. The main feature is the uniformly low value of time, although these values were derived from bus users; for car users, the values are higher (by an average of 35% for the three SP studies). The elasticity results are less consistent. In two of the SP studies high values are achieved because our sample under-represents non-traders, who are perfectly inelastic. In the two disaggregate RP studies, low values are achieved because generated trips are excluded and rail fares in West Yorkshire were at relatively low levels (particularly in 1990). Overall, a rail fare elasticity in the region of -0.6 to -0.9 is typical.

Table 7.7: Daily Trip Rates per Thousand Population (0-2km approx.)

New stations/services already opened		New stations/services yet to be opened	
West Yorkshire - 9 new stations	19.4	Nottingham - Worksop	18.6
Walsall - Hednesford	12.3	Leicester- Burton-upon-Trent	28.7
Edinburgh - Bathgate	29.9	Clitheroe	16.9
Aberdare	18.8	Brighouse/Elland	32.3

Source: Ref. 14.

Table 7.8: Comparison of Rail Fare Elasticities and Values of Rail In-Vehicle Time by County (1990).

Area	Type of Model	Fare Elasticity	Value of Time (p/min)
West Yorkshire: 39 stations	Aggregate: Direct Demand	-0.83	N/A
Greater Manchester: 33 stations	Aggregate: Trip End	-0.66	N/A
West Yorkshire: 3 corridors, 1981	Disaggregate: RP (work only)	-0.34	3.0
West Yorkshire: 2 corridors, 1990	Disaggregate: RP	-0.26	2.8
Leicestershire	Disaggregate: SP	-1.51	1.9
Nottinghamshire	Disaggregate: SP	-1.99	1.1 to 1.9
Lancashire	Disaggregate: SP	-0.70	2.3

An important trade-off has been identified. As model complexity increases, specification error tends to reduce (as models become more detailed) but measurement error tends to increase (as model input requirements increase). The optimum, in terms of accuracy and level of complexity depends on how detailed the model results are required to be. For the three levels of investment identified above the following methods are suggested:

(i) For one-off new stations, forecasting may be based on a trip rate model, preferably locally-calibrated. If there is no suitable existing local station then a trip rate or direct demand model may be transferred from elsewhere and/or a stated intentions survey undertaken, but checks against possible bias are necessary, using either an existing RP or SP mode choice model.

(ii) For packages of new stations, a direct demand model for existing local stations should be developed and applied to predict the usage of potential new stations. For the 'best' sites, an SP mode choice model might be applied in conjunction with existing origin/ destination information to determine the extent of mode switching (currently being done in Lancashire). Where a network of local rail stations does not exist, reliance would have to be put on SP or 'imported' RP approaches.

(iii) For major new services, requiring section 56 grant, disaggregate approaches are required. Where possible these should be based on RP models, although supplemented by SP data to improve data and statistical efficiency, as is occurring in a major study of Trans-pennine rail services at present.[17] In many cases, it will be necessary to rely solely on SP data. Ideally, the model should be applied with disaggregate time and cost information (the 'sample enumeration' approach) but more usually use will be made of aggregate engineering or stated intentions data. Where possible, some checks with RP data should be made.

References

1. Aldridge, D. and Preston, J.M. (1991) "Greater Manchester PTE New Railway Station Demand Prediction Model". Technical Note 292, Institute for Transport Studies, University of Leeds.
2. Bates, J.J. (1988) "Econometric Issues in Stated Preference Analysis". Jnl. of Trans. Econ. & Pol. 22, 56-69.
3. Fowkes, T. and J. Preston (1991) "Novel Approaches to Forecasting the Demand for New Local Rail Services". Transpn. Res., 25A, 4, 209-218.
4. Kennedy, G. (1990) "The BR Approach". In KPMG Peat Marwick McLintock Ltd " Seminar on Developing Local Rail Services - Speakers' Notes". York, November.
5. Knight, J., Blackledge, D., Brocklebank, P. and Rasbash, D. (1989) "The Reintroduction of Suburban Rail Passenger Services in Staffordshire and the West Midlands". PTRC Summer Annual Meeting, Seminar D, Brighton.
6. Nash, C.A., Preston, J.M. and Hopkinson, P.G. (1990) "Applications of

Stated Preference Analysis". Department of Transport Conference on Longer Term Issues. July.

7. Nash, C.A. and Preston, J.M. (1991) "Appraisal of Rail Investment Projects: Recent British Experience". *Transport Reviews.* pp. 295-309.

8. Owen, A.D. and Phillips, G.D.A. (1987) "The Characteristics of Railway Passenger Demand". *Jnl. Trans. Econ. & Pol.* 21 pp. 231-253.

9. Preston, J.M. (1987a) "The Potential for Opening New Local Rail Stations". *PTRC Summer Annual Meeting,* Seminar B, Bath.

10. Preston, J.M. (1987b) "The Evaluation of New Local Rail Stations in West Yorkshire". PhD Thesis, School of Economic Studies, University of Leeds.

11. Preston, J.M. (1991a) "Demand Forecasting for New Local Rail Stations and Services". *Jnl. Trans. Econ. & Pol.,* 25 pp. 183-202.

12. Preston, J.M. (1991b) "New Stations and Services". In Fowkes, A.S. and Nash, C.A. (Eds) "Analysing Demand for Rail Travel". Avebury, Aldershot.

13. Preston, J.M. (1991c) "Analysis of Proposed Ribble Valley Rail Services. Final Report". Unpublished. January.

14. Preston, J.M. (1991d) "A Note on the Traffic Generation of New Local Rail Services". Unpublished. April.

15. Preston, J.M. and Nash, C.A. (1986) "Some Guidelines for Evaluating New Local Rail Stations". Working Paper 228. Institute for Transport Studies, University of Leeds.

16. Railway Development Society (1989) "A-Z of Rail Re-Openings". RDS, Great Bookham, Surrey.

17. Sully, J. (1990) "Pennine Report", *Mod. Rlys.* 47 pp. 457-459.

18. Taylor, D. (1990) "The Demand for New Rail Stations, Molescroft: A Case Study". MSc Dissertation, Institute for Transport Studies, University of Leeds. Unpublished.

19. Transportation Planning Associates (TPA) and the Institute for Transport Studies (ITS). (1990) "Brighouse-Elland Rail Study: Final Report". Unpublished. May.

20. Wardman, M. (1991) "Stated Preference Methods and Travel Demand Forecasting: An Examination of the Scale Factor Problem". *Transpn. Res.,* 25A, 2/3, 79-89.

21. Whitehead, P. (1981) "Estimating the Effects on Revenue of Rail Service Changes". *PTRC Summer Annual Meeting,* Seminar K, Warwick.

ACKNOWLEDGEMENT: The research into new stations and services has been a team effort at Leeds University's Institute for Transport Studies. The work was initiated by Chris Nash and a number of people have worked on subsequent projects including Tony Fowkes, Mark Wardman, Ken Mason, Eileen Hill and Dave Aldridge, as well as MSc students Glyn Hockenhull, Andy Clarke, Alan Peakall and David Taylor.

8. Planning New High Speed Rail Links - Lessons and Questions From the London - Channel Tunnel Connection

Malcolm Buchanan

Introduction

The previous two chapters have shown how demand is usually analysed for relatively small changes or local schemes. For large projects, however, the position is quite different, and politics are much more important. New railways have to be planned under antiquated parliamentary procedures which were designed to deal with the rival railway lines of private sector promoters in the nineteenth century. The procedures are therefore merely concerned with granting or amending the powers requested by the promoters and not with determining whether the scheme is justifiable or whether there are better alternatives. In the days of the railway entrepreneurs these were matters for them. Today with public investment required and with external costs and benefits considered important, they are very much matters of public concern.

On the roads, however, over twenty years of controversy have ensured that proponents of and objectors to new motorways and trunk roads in Britain are reasonably familiar with the rules of the game. Both know the expected sorts of research, planning and consultation procedures, what are reasonable environmental and cost benefit cases, and how the inquiry procedure works. Though they may still object in principle and/or in detail, most protesters must feel as they leave the witness box that they have at least had a chance to put their case against a proposal and that they clearly understand what that proposal is.

None of this has unfortunately been true of the planning of Britain's first major trunk railway of this century - the high speed link between London and the Channel Tunnel. Undue secrecy, lobbying, incomplete and misleading proposals, rapidly escalating cost estimates, dubious economics and new levels of NIMBYism (NIMBY=Not In My Back Yard) have been the order of the day. This state of affairs has arisen partly because of the antiquated parliamentary procedures, partly because of changing requirements as to who would be constructing the line and how it would be funded, and partly because of BR's single-mindedness determination to press ahead with its own scheme.

The changing requirements within which the high speed line and second Channel Tunnel Terminal have had to be developed have reflected diminishing expectations regarding the viability of the project. Flushed with its success in promoting the Channel Tunnel as a private sector project, the government initially insisted that BR should go into partnership with the private sector and build the high speed link and second terminal as a commercial venture without public investment. So insistent was the government on this point that it inserted a clause in the Channel Tunnel Act specifically preventing subsidy. A great deal of time and effort was accordingly spent by BR in selecting a commercial partner, but the sums done by the bidders clearly showed the project to be unviable as a private sector venture especially if BR insisted on its plan for a terminal underneath King's Cross with a long and expensive access tunnel beneath central and inner London. Some of the private sector bidders withdrew, some warned BR they were of the view that Stratford might be a cheaper option, but others stayed in the race, presumably in the hope that the government would relent and make some public money available. The partners finally selected by BR did not remain partners very long. Realising that (at the time) the government meant what it said, the consortium broke up and BR, perhaps to its relief, was left to pursue its original plans. In subsequently inviting BR to review the various alternative links, using its Rail Link Project Team, the Department of Transport relaxed the rules. This time there was no requirement for private sector participation and it was hinted that whilst public money could not be made available to subsidise Channel Tunnel passengers, it could be available for any commuters carried on the line and for any consequent benefits to commuters on other lines.

BR's single mindedness in pursuing and developing virtually the same channel tunnel rail link and terminal through these changing circumstances presumably reflects its professional judgement that this is the best option for itself and the country. The same commercial arguments which caused its former partners to withdraw and which in turn led both Rail Europe and Arup to conclude that they did not after all have commercial options, seem to have caused few qualms to BR. BR presumably believes that even if the scheme is not commercially viable, public money spent on it will be worthwhile. But BR's espousal of a scheme which so completely fails to satisfy its commercial remit and which is in practice also difficult to justify in terms of benefits to commuters, raises several questions:

1) Is there some greater good, not taken into account within BR's varying remits, which ought to be built into the planning process?
2) How can new lines be funded and promoted in a way which allows some public sector investment but retains private sector disciplines?
3) How can the planning process be re-arranged to be both more open and more rigorous?
4) Given the present four alternative options for the high speed link to the Channel - which is the best and what is the best course for BR and the Government to adopt?

Objectives and Evaluation Procedures
The answer to the first of the questions raised by the present situation is that high speed rail links are merely transport investments like roads or airports. Whilst it is true that their effects may be rather different (e.g. on land use), and whilst some of these effects lie outside BR's remit, they do not raise issues different in kind to those raised by motorways, for which practical and acceptable planning assessment and inquiry procedures already exist. The difference in the nature of BR vis-a-vis the Department of Transport, and more general "benefits" to the economy are irrelevant. The real case for investing in a new high speed link is to produce benefits to users (passengers and freight) whilst minimising adverse effects and preferably contributing positively to planning and environmental policies. This has to be achieved within a further important objective of minimising any requirement for public sector funds. This need not mean that there should be no call on public funds at all, but it should mean that if government money is required a good social cost/benefit return on it must be demonstrated in exactly the same way as it has to be for motorways. One crucial difference from motorway investment, however, arises from the fact that rail users pay fares or charges. The revenue yielded, like any revenue from related property developments, can minimise any call on public sector funds and thus make the requirement easier to justify (not forgetting that higher fares are a disbenefit to those who pay them).

The implication of explicitly recognising these objectives in planning new rail links is that they should be evaluated and justified within a tough and rigorous cost benefit framework in the way set out in SACTRA's Economic Evaluation Comparability Study. A further implication is that the amount of public money which may be justifiable can be determined as that which would give the government a good return (say a benefit/cost ratio of 1.5). Some certainty that government money able to earn this sort of return would be likely to be forthcoming would then leave BR and any commercial partners free to plan and manage the project in a more commercial way instead of having to go cap in hand to government on every commercial decision. Moreover such a financial framework would remove any temptation for BR to go for the best railway solution and ignore the commercial and cost benefit realities in the hope that the government might just be persuaded to fund something more extravagant.

Public Scrutiny

The planning process required to put these procedures into effect must plainly be built around some kind of public scrutiny of the complete proposal so that objectors to it and those who have alternative proposals may have a chance to test the strengths of BR's arguments and to put their own points of view. The sort of scrutiny required seems more likely to resemble a public inquiry than a hearing before a parliamentary committee since such committees are unlikely to have either the time or the expertise necessary fully to expose the issues involved.

Several procedural matters will be important if the planning process is to work well and fairly. The first is that BR should be compelled to define complete, free-standing options. A Channel Tunnel Terminal underneath King's Cross with no justified means of getting international trains to it (as proposed in the King's Cross Railways Bill) is not a freestanding option and could never be justified on its own. Moreover a decision to invest in such a terminal would in effect pre-empt any subsequent decision on the route. On the other hand a high speed link on its own, designed to serve Waterloo (and a later second terminal), would have been a freestanding option and might well have been justified, but has curiously never been proposed.

The definition of a complete option also implies that joint costs should be made explicit. In appraising the proposed High Speed Link and Channel Tunnel Terminal at King's Cross, where there are joint costs with both Thameslink and Inter-City, a complete option must therefore include the effects on Thameslink and Inter-City services; if rival options exist which do not involve King's Cross, they should be compared with equivalent Thameslink and Inter-City schemes. In each case, however, the same rules must apply and all schemes with joint costs must be included since such costs, by definition, cannot be allocated.

The evaluation of a high speed link and terminal also implies the definition of a "do minimum". For the high speed link and second Channel Tunnel Terminal the "do minimum" had plainly to include the first terminal at Waterloo and to take account of the maximum international service which might be operated to Waterloo in the absence of a second terminal - an under-researched subject. Decisions had also to be taken as to whether committed "do minimum" schemes should include the Jubilee Line Extension, Crossrail and the proposed Chelsea-Hackney tube.

BR might well argue that early exposure of its plans to public scrutiny might give valuable commercial information to rivals such as airlines or coach operators. However, the implementation timescales of high speed links mean that rival operators will anyway have years in which to research and formulate competing strategies. Concern about commercial secrecy is more significant regarding property blight but here the issues are no different to those faced by motorway planners and cannot be allowed to stand in the way of public scrutiny. Nor should commercial secrecy be allowed to become a means of concealing from rival operators and the public the full scale of the public sector support being requested. Use of the taxpayers money carries the penalty that the taxpayer has a right to know what is being spent and why.

Towards a Decision on the High Speed Link and Second London Terminal

Given these lessons from Britain's experience so far in attempting to plan and implement a high speed link and second terminal for services between the Channel Tunnel and London, what should be government reaction to the four main proposals illustrated in Figure 8.1?

o the BR proposal to King's Cross (the KX option)[2]

o the Rail Europe proposal to Stratford (the RE option)[1]

o the Arup proposal to Stratford and thence to King's Cross (the AR option)

o the Newham/Buchanan proposal to Stratford (the NB option).

It is tempting to argue that the government should simply get on and make a firm decision - better to make some choice, like the French, than to dither endlessly over what will clearly eventually become a vital piece of transport infrastructure. But this popular line of argument ignores the facts that first the amount of public investment involved is very high (enough for example to provide several major conurbations with their own metro systems), second that those evaluations which

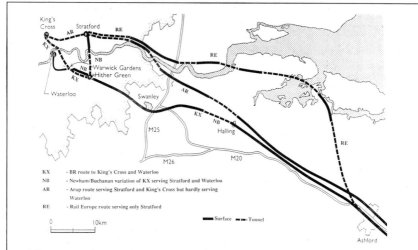

Fig. 8.1   Alternative Options for the High Speed Link Between London and the Channel Tunnel.

have been carried out suggest that even counting all the benefits to international as well as commuter passengers, the investment will give a very poor rate of return, and third that there is a real and well founded controversy over the best option. BR's preferred route and terminal is by no means the obvious choice.

The government therefore has a clear duty not to be rushed into premature decisions by BR but to examine carefully within the cost/benefit framework whether and (more interestingly) when there is a case first for a high speed link and then for a second terminal and which is the best complete option.

At a strategic level, then, one must plan using order-of-magnitude cost data (see chapter 17) and preliminary estimates of demand developed from examining existing markets (here, that for travel between Britain and Western Europe). The travel markets need to be split up by journey purpose (and hence by sensitivity to time and cost, so that elasticities can be estimated), and by origin and destination. Rail's mode share between Central London and Central Paris is likely to be much higher than between Wales and Spain, but the relative sizes of the markets also need to be taken into account.

Given this, then, one can argue the relative merits of different schemes (even if they are only outlined broadly, as in Figure 8.1). In terms of capital costs there is no doubt that the NB option is the cheapest. Its relatively short length of tunnel (25 kilometres) makes its high speed link far cheaper than any of the rivals, whilst its single, surface terminal at Stratford costs only about one third of the works proposed at King's Cross. Bearing in mind that terminal costs account for about 25% of the total project costs this is a significant advantage. The KX option has a capital cost 20-50% higher than the NB option (depending on whether a free-standing Thameslink is included with the latter). The most expensive option is clearly the AR option which incurs double, sub-surface terminal costs in London (Stratford and King's Cross) and the extra length of tunnel between Stratford and King's Cross. Whilst the AR option must be far more expensive than the KX option, its benefits can be little better since it ends at the same place and it does little for the 50% of international trains that will serve Waterloo. It must therefore be inferior to the KX option. The RE option must have similar terminal costs to the NB option but a far higher link cost since it has more than double the amount of tunnel. Moreover, the RE option does nothing for the international trains that will continue to serve Waterloo. It follows that it must be inferior to the NB option and that the choice of the best link and terminal must therefore lie between the NB option and the KX option. In making this choice the critical question is whether the extra capital cost of around £1 billion is worth paying for the advantages of serving King's Cross rather than Stratford.

In addressing this question the most important issue which arises is whether any extra revenue would be earned through serving King's Cross. This depends on the relative journey times offered from the Continent not only to the whole of the London area but also to the rest of the country. On this count King's Cross might be thought to have a major advantage especially as Inter-City passengers on the East Coast Main Line (ECML) would have an easy interchange at King's Cross. However, the advantages of King's Cross for London-bound passengers are very much less than are commonly supposed (typically being under 10 minutes), and vary depending upon the exact destination within the capital.

For travel beyond London the NB option has a clear advantage for East Anglia, and CrossRail will make it more convenient for much of Western Region. For services from Waterloo and London Bridge there is little to choose between the two. For services from Victoria the KX option has a 12 minute advantage and for services involving an interchange via King's Cross/St Pancras/Euston it has a 20 minute advantage. However for most of these latter passengers it is BR's intention to provide through trains and the same or more frequent through services could be provided via Stratford.

For onward journeys by road Stratford with its planned direct connections to the M25 and North and South Circular Roads will not only offer quicker journey times than King's Cross or Waterloo but will also be able to accommodate the required parking. It may therefore be concluded that what Stratford might lose in rail passengers it will more than gain in passengers seeking road access and this is important since it is the car market to Heathrow and Gatwick with which the new high speed link must compete for revenue.

If the time saving advantages of the KX option relative to the NB option are small, but the extra cost is substantial, then the conventional cost benefit case must favour the NB option. Three further matters reinforce this case. The first is that in environmental terms the NB option is clearly superior. Both options are identical from the Channel Tunnel to Hither Green but from North of that point the impact of the NB option is almost wholly positive. It will lead to the transformation of an area of inner city dereliction at Stratford and it will offer the opportunity to construct a terminal of unparalleled environmental quality. By contrast the environmental problems associated with the KX option are severe. At Warwick Gardens the construction of a sub-surface junction in a dense residential area will cause disruption and blight. At King's Cross itself the KX option requires the demolition of four Grade II listed buildings and over a 100 dwelling units, and it has a severe impact on two conservation areas.

In terms of planning and development the case for the NB option is even stronger. The construction of a terminal at King's Cross runs counter to the statutory Local Plan and has been vigorously opposed on these grounds. By contrast at Stratford the terminal accords with the Local Plan of the London Borough of Newham and with the strategic planning advice of both the LPAC and SERPLAN organisations. The King's Cross terminal is expected to be largely neutral in its effects on the King's Cross development but by contrast a terminal at Stratford is seen as a means of unscrambling the planning stagnation on the Stratford railway land site. Freight forwarders, hotels, etc. would quickly seek locations in the Stratford area and they could be followed by businesses seeking European headquarters with good access to Paris and Brussels, by conference centres and by new European institutions. These developments in turn would encourage the growth of more offices, business parks and retail activities, all of which would be directly attributable to the terminal and very unlikely to happen in its absence.

As far as effects on other rail services are concerned, however, the NB option tunnel from Hither Green to Canning Town will also release suburban rail capacity in inner London for additional passenger

94

services. Although primarily a passenger railway, freight activity will also affect any new line built. Here, however, the requirement is for an additional Thames crossing. Under the KX option some freight trains will virtually circumnavigate central London, travelling via the West London line to reach Temple Mills yard adjacent to Stratford.

On financial, cost benefit, environmental and planning grounds the NB option is therefore clearly preferable to the KX option. The issue which really faces the Government is that of timing. The early construction of a second Channel Tunnel Terminal is in many ways premature. The first terminal is not yet constructed, its capacity limitations may prove to have been overstated, the demand must be somewhat uncertain and the financial case for an early second terminal looks poor. But this case will improve as demand rises. On the other hand the case for an enhanced ThamesLink service, currently held back by the KX option, looks to be strong and the case for a high speed link on its own has not been explored. The most prudent course would therefore appear to be:

1) implement a modest and cost effective ThamesLink upgrading scheme;
2) examine the case for the High Speed Link serving Waterloo on its own;
3) allow the King's Cross development to proceed;
4) bring the Waterloo terminal into service and exploit its capacity and its revenue earning potential to the full;
5) construct the High Speed Link to Hither Green with a connection to Waterloo;
6) extend the link to a second terminal at Stratford when justified.

We must wait and see how political pressures affect the development of this new line.

References

1. Glover, J. (1991) "Rail Europe - a Continental Railway", *Transp. Economist* 18 pp.9-14.
2. Perren, B. et al. (1990) "Channel Connection", Supplement Issued with Rail magazine.

Postscript: On 9th October 1991, the Secretary of State for Transport announced that the Government favoured the Arup route[1] for the Channel Tunnel Rail Link, partly because of the opportunities it presented for regenerating the East Thames Corridor. British Rail suggested that the decision was prompted more by concern about the effects of the link on voting intentions in marginal constituencies, and published its Rail Link Project (RLP) team's assessment of the four options. This report regrettably only compares the three alternatives to its preferred option, giving no complete appraisal of the latter, its timing or the relative timing of the link and the second London terminal. The RLP team's report is also based on an assumption that only a share of the total cost of the King's Cross Railway Bill works (£1.4Bn) should be allocated to the international terminal, which is then assessed in isolation from plans for Thameslink services. The report also contains disputed figures about land value enhancement gains at Stratford and King's Cross. Even with these problems, however, the RLP report questions BR's strong espousal of King's Cross. Its conclusions are summarised in Table 1 and indicate that, even on their own figures, the Newham/Buchanan option had an Net Present Value (NPV - see chapter 21) within £120M (only 3.5%) of the BR option; this is clearly within the accuracy of the calculations.

The bottom half of the table shows that alternative assumptions about land enhancement values and cost allocations at King's Cross change the option ranking, since the NB option would have had a capital cost of £880M less than the BR option, and an NPV £400M better. Perhaps had agreed figures been more widely available, it would have been much harder for the Secretary of State to reject the BR route and choose the politically-softer but more expensive Arup route. Instead, BR now faces the prospect of a delayed high speed line only able to serve half the international trains and two of the three terminals, at a capital cost which is £1.5Bn more than the NB option and with an NPV which is £1.2Bn worse. However, it is the potential delay to the project that worries many people, especially Eurotunnel. With such disadvantages, the planning benefits in the East Thames corridor will need to be very substantial, whilst the political nature of the decision, have been underscored.

Reference: 1. Moore, G. (1991) "Arup's Route to London", Rail 160 pp. 34-35.

Table 8.1. The RLP Team's Evaluation of the Options for the Rail Link and Second London Terminal

Cost/Benefit	British Rail (KX)	Arup (AR)	Newham/ Buchanan(NB)	Rail Europe (RE)
Termini Served	Wat, KX	SF,KX	Wat,SF	SF
Figures from the RLP Report				
Revenues & Benefits*	BR	BR-205	BR-580	BR-760
Route Costs	-2815	-3045	-2455	-3080
Terminal Costs	-610	-860	-490	-490
Freight Costs	0	-100	0	-150
Property Costs	-140	- 240	-160	-220
Total NPV	BR-3565	BR-4450	BR-3685	BR-4700
Difference from BR	0	- 885	-120	-1135
Adjustment to the RLP Figures				
Land Value Enhancement	40	120	140	130
Share of unallocated £570M costs at King's Cross	-419	-419	0	0
Comparison with the NB Option				
Capital Cost	879	1559	0	835
NPV	-399	-1204	0	-1025

*: BR is the NPV of the revenue and benefits of the BR option, a figure not revealed. However, it can be seen that it must exceed £3.565Bn to make the project worthwhile.

The English Channel Tunnel terminal squeezed between the North Downs and Cheriton. The impact on the environment is significant. *Both photographs courtesy of Eurotunnel Ltd./QA Photos.*

Under the channel in one of the crossover caverns. A tunnel boring machine is shown with the temporary construction railway, clean air supply and power supplies that have enabled the construction of this vital undersea link.

MODERN RAILWAYS

Published every month,
Modern Railways is
Britain's foremost
magazine devoted to
railway developments
in Britain and overseas.
With its regular columnists,
such as Roger Ford, the
Magazine provides
excellent coverage on a wide
range of railway related
subjects.

MODERN RAILWAYS

Edited by Ken Cordner
Published on the fourth
Thursday of each month.
Subscription rates (as at 1 August
1991): Home: £21.00 (one year);
£40.00 (two years); Overseas
(Surface Mail): £29.00 (one year).
Air Mail rates available on application.

ORDER FORM to:

Ian Allan Subscriptions Dept (Ref OS225), Select Subscriptions, Northbridge
Road, Berkhamsted, Hertfordshire HP4 1ST. Telephone: 0442 876661 quoting
Ref OS225.
I wish to take out a subscription to Modern Railways starting with the
..................dated issue. I enclose £........(payable to Ian Allan Ltd) or please
debit my Access/Trustcard/Visa number:

....

Signed:.................................Card Expiry Date:...............................
Name:.................................Address:..
.................................Postcode:..................................

Visions of the future: a suburban B5000 bogied train designed by RFS Industries. Reduction in weight of the bogie will allow higher speeds with lower track forces. *Courtesy: RFS Industries Group.*

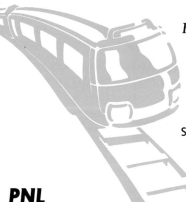

The 12:25 Neerpelt—Antwerpen Centraal forms part of the SNCB RIT is seen next to a DB freight of swap bodies and containers from Neuss—Antwerpen Schienpoort. *Courtesy: David Haydock.*

The Passenger Transport Executives are considerable sponsors of local rail services. Significant amounts of money have been spent on new rolling stock, stations, new and reopened passenger routes. Greater Manchester PTE helped BR to purchase new class 142 DMU's like the one shown which is at New Mills Central.

9. Recent Developments in Public Transport Network Modelling

Nigel G Harris

What Are Network Models?
Network models are computer-based simulations of transport networks, in which the network configuration is an important element; they are thus particularly important where the network exhibits considerable connectivity, where changes on one link have important effects elsewhere on the system. Although subject to simplification, the networks are comprised of **zones** (where traffic enters and leaves the system), **nodes** (which may be seen as junctions in the network) and **links** (joining the nodes to each other and to the zones). Associated with each link are a number of characteristics e.g. directionality (i.e. one-way or two-way), length, time required to traverse it, and mode (e.g. walk, car, rail etc.), whilst associated with the network is a **demand matrix** of trips between every zone as origin and every other zone as destination. An **algorithm** is used within the software to allocate the trips in the demand matrix to the network, and this requires a number of parameters (e.g. the Value Of Time) to be input. Network modelling is therefore especially suitable in major urban areas where the rail network is not merely radial (e.g. London, the Rhein-Ruhr), and where route choice and good survey bases exist.

The Uses of Network Models
The main uses of network models may be seen to be:
(i)   the analysis of the spatial variability of demand, the identification of pinch points, and the optimum allocation of resources[11];
(ii)   a cheap environment for testing changes to transport infrastructure; and
(iii) providing a method of disaggregation for demand forecasts.

Results for the first two problems can alternatively be derived from econometric modelling work, but only at a much more global level; however, variations in demand between areas and periods may be sufficiently great so as to invalidate conclusions drawn from such global analyses. For instance, London Underground Ltd produces over 9bn seat miles p.a. (and over 2.5bn in the peaks) whilst demand is only 4bn and 2bn respectively, which does not indicate a problem, but it is well-known that many parts of the network are severely congested for many hours of the day (see maps in the Central London Rail Study[5]). For instance, the Liverpool Street - Bank section of the Central line carries, on average, twice as many passengers during the three-hour a.m. peak as seats are provided.

The second main use of network models is in option analysis, right down from scenario testing (see ref. 15, ch. 8) to examining the effects of changes in train service levels. It is much more cost-effective to simulate options on a computer in the office rather than trying to experiment with the passengers themselves.

A third use is in disaggregate demand forecasting, where known changes in network or services can be combined with matrix manipulations on the base matrix to produce demand forecasts for every link and node on the system; such information is particularly useful as a management tool for a wide range of planning purposes e.g. in staff requirements, capacity enhancements, services changes, evacuation times etc.

Network Models: History to 1980
Network modelling is a data-hungry process, and therefore did not develop until the first computer revolution in the 1950s. As a recognised technique, it had its origins in the early 1960s, and soon came to be used as an important part of the evaluation framework for new roads, where it has long been recognised that new roads impact on the demand for existing ones (indeed, the *raison d'etre* of bypasses is precisely to reduce demand on the existing road network). The 1970s saw developments to algorithms away from an **all-or-nothing** approach (in which all traffic on any Origin : Destination pair is allocated to the route with the smallest generalised cost) to **multi-routeing** approaches (where some traffic is allocated to the 'shortest' route, but other proportions are allocated to other routes with similar g.c.s). Algorithms also began to include public transport services, where assumptions are required as to standard parameters such as weightings for walking and waiting.

Types of Network Models
It is important at this stage to distinguish between two main types of network models, which we may call zone-based and station-based. In zone-based models (of which the LTS model[16] is one of the best-known)(and see also ch. 5 of ref. 15), the region under study is split into

98

zones corresponding to political or administrative areas, for which data (e.g. on population) is readily available. A trip generation sub-model is required to determine the number of journeys generated by such a population (or attracted by the employment of the areas) in the modelled time-period, and a modal split model is used to allocate the trips between modes, before assignment to the network occurs. Whilst this has the advantage of being soundly based on facts, this extra modelling stage introduces potential for error before the assignment stage occurs.

Station-based modelling, on the other hand, takes station entries as fixed, and assignment occurs directly. For public transport operators with good survey bases, this will provide more accurate data from which to work, but it does suffer from the disadvantage that some trip-making occurs outside the model e.g. park and ride to station A may be replaced in reality (but not in the model) by park and ride to station B. Moreover, modelling the impact of the introduction of a new station, for instance, can only be done explicitly outside the model e.g. by using the results of chapter 7.

Developments in the 1980s
Three key factors have provided the stimuli for the development of network models in the 1980s - the second computer revolution, an increase in environmental awareness, and a significant growth in the use of public transport in some major conurbations.

The second computer revolution meant that by 1990, you could do calculations on a stand-alone personal computer which would have required a mini-computer, if not a mainframe, 10 years earlier. This put network analysis within the reach of an increasing number of authorities and organisations, even if few of them realised the opportunity. For those who did, costs fell dramatically.

The increase in environmental awareness (which took place in the late 1980s in Britain, but five or ten years earlier in some other European countries) had the effect of moving transport up the political agenda. It also increased the importance of public transport relative to private transport, demanded environmental outputs from transport modelling (such as pollution emitted) and, backed up by strong NIMBYism (NIMBY = Not In My Back Yard) based on an increasingly-affluent society, created much greater public interest in proposals for changes to transport infrastructure.

In some countries, public transport (but notably rail) enjoyed a renaissance in the 1980s, fuelled by increasing road congestion and the heightened environmental awareness already mentioned. Where this coincided with significant employment growth (which, in an era of continued deindustrialisation, was primarily in areas dominated by office employment) railways increased not only their patronage with new customers but even their mode share at the expense of private transport (see table 1.4 of ref. 12). Such pressure on London's network led to Government action in the form of the Central London and East London Rail Studies. By late 1990, a major extension to the Jubilee line was already being debated in Parliament, with commitment for an East-West Crossrail RER-type scheme to follow it, whilst elsewhere in Britain, there were a large number of light rail proposals; those for Sheffield and, more especially Manchester, were making progress through the planning and financial maze (see chapter 4).

In addition to specific schemes, the British Department of Transport also initiated major studies into four areas of particular transport difficulty within London; although primarily intended to be road-based, public opinion forced the inclusion of public transport improvements to the reports on NE, SW and two areas of South London[6,7,8,9] (see also ref. 3 for more detail of the method used). All these put demand on the facilities available for network modelling, and encouraged methodological developments.

So these key factors provided the impetus for three significant developments in network modelling - better graphics, better algorithms, and improved methods of dealing with public transport congestion.

Graphics
The widespread availability of colour monitors for personal computers (pcs) has enabled graphical output to become popular. The ease with which network data can be visualised when seen graphically is such that an entirely new method of working - the mouse - has been developed as a new computer tool. Such progress has been reinforced by the entry into the market of new network modelling software, in which the mouse/graphics interface is a key feature[14,18]. This has stimulated competition amongst other program suites previously using plotting only for map-based information[2].

However, ease of data entry and network understanding are not the only major attributes of a graphically-based system. For complicated networks, where the data-set gets large, the possibility of undetected errors within the data is significant, and visual display often highlights such errors far more easily than columns of figures can. Moreover, the requirement to work with numerical descriptions of nodes may be reduced.

Algorithms

We have already seen that the first algorithms (such as those developed by Burrell, and Dial) were all-or-nothing; this weakness has been removed more slowly on the public transport side of network modelling than on the highway side, and it was not until the late 1980s that proportional assignment algorithms became available[4] and began to be used[17].

The early algorithms, however, had other problems, chiefly in dealing with particular public transport assignment problems such as fares, which are rarely a linear function of distance travelled. Stage-based fares have tended to be treated by analogy to a function of the form

$$F = B + a_1 D$$

$$\text{where} \quad F = \text{fare}$$
$$B = \text{boarding penalty}$$
$$D = \text{distance}$$
$$\text{and} \quad a_1 = \text{constant.}$$

but most of the British metropolitan areas, as well as many centres abroad (notably the whole of Holland) use a zonal fares system, where this approach is unsatisfactory. The existence of an annular fare zone system in London where, as we have seen, a great amount of network modelling was being carried out, stimulated development in this field, and latest thoughts seem to centre around the allocation of nodes or links to fare-zones, since the number of fare zones traversed is a basic indicator of the fare due. This problem, however, remains acute for the time being for orbital network developments - such as London Underground's East London Line extensions - where not only is an unwanted trip into and out of the Central area avoided, but so is that part of the fare.

Fares, however, are not the only algorithmic problem facing software writers. On routes where not all services stop at all nodes, combination rules are required to determine what is the real frequency available to passengers. In some cases, the underlying market research is not always to hand e.g. it is often assumed that passengers will not board a service to a destination if a following departure is timed to arrive first, but in severe weather, on an unreliable line, some (unknown number of) passengers with no pressing hurry are quite likely to take the first train that actually appears.

Quite complicated options may be apparent to passengers which involve decision-making en route e.g. it is rarely possible to get bus and train services from the same spot, so a choice has to be made as to where to stand in real life, a choice that needs to be modelled. Gradually, the assumptions that have hitherto underlain network modelling (e.g. rational behaviour and perfect passenger information) are being tested.

Congestion

Foremost amongst algorithmic improvements, perhaps, is the development of software to treat overcrowding on public transport. In the 1970s and 1980s, congestion on public transport was sufficiently negligible (except on the Hong Kong metro system) to be completely ignored, but traffic and tighter resource management had made congestion endemic by the end of the decade. Software developments have had to take account of passengers' options to

(a) travel by an alternative route;
(b) suppress the demand for that trip (either by making a motorised trip by non-motorised means, or by moving out of the area under study altogether); or
(c) travel at an alternative time.

Coping with (a) has been relatively easy for software writers. The approach generally adopted has been to determine a perceived speed : flow relationship from market research, to apply the resulting delays to the base times, and then to recalculate routes based on the revised network. This becomes an iterative process which should converge eventually (see Fig. 2 of ref. 10), although 'flipping' between two adjacent and heavily-congested routes may occur, where traffic takes one route in the even-numbered iterations and the other in the odd-numbered iterations.

London Underground were amongst the first to incorporate demand suppression into this framework, with a program module which, for every Origin : Destination pair, compared the times for successive iterations, and applied an elasticity to the base trip matrix to give a new trip matrix for the next iteration[10]. This process also works in reverse, in that trips can be generated if congestion improves between iterations. In a zone-based, rather than a station-based, model, this problem is reduced (but not eliminated), since traffic can switch between modes; it cannot otherwise, however, be modelled to follow the industrialist moving his factory to a less-congested part of the country, or a trip being replaced by a non-motorised one.

Congestion has also become of concern, not only on public transport vehicles, but elsewhere in the public transport operators' domain. Underground railway operators in Britain have faced tougher safety legislation following the fire at King's Cross in 1987, requiring them to be able to evacuate stations within 6 minutes. This necessitates an improved understanding about pedestrian flow characteristics, not only at individual stations, but also across the network as a whole (see refs. 13 and 11 respectively).

The problem of time-switching is still under investigation. Little market research is available to show how many passengers (commuters, in particular, since it is obviously in the peak periods that the worst congestion occurs) *can* change their travel time and, of those, how many *would* do so, and what incentives they might need, and which direction they might change in (earlier or later).

Further Developments

Under investigation at present is the dynamic reassignment of travellers i.e. modelling the ability of travellers to alter their journey en route dependent upon the congestion encountered. This and the time-switching issue are both under investigation for highway networks (e.g. ref. 1), but not yet for public transport networks, yet this is an important area for operators of congested systems to understand - how will their passengers respond?

References

1. Ahn, B-H & Shin, J-Y (1991) "Vehicle-Routeing with Time Windows and Time-Varying Congestion", *Jnl. Operational. Res. Soc.* 42 pp 393-400.
2. Bach, M. & Benschop, J. (1990) "Developments in Transportation Planning Software: MVGRAF - an Interactive Network Graphics Program", *Traff. Engng. & Ctrl.* 31 pp. 215-220.
3. Coombe, R.D., Forshaw, I.R. & Bamford, T.J.C. (1990) "Assessment on the London Assessment Studies", *Traff. Engng. & Ctrl.* 31 pp. 510-518.
4. de Cea, J., Bunster, J.P., Zubleta, L. & Florian, M (1988) Optimal Strategies and Optimal Routes in Public Transit Assignment Models: an Empirical Comparison", *Traff. Engng. & Ctrl.* 29 pp. 520-526.
5. Department of Transport, British Rail Network SouthEast, London Regional Transport and London Underground Ltd. (1989) "Central London Rail Study".
6. Department of Transport (1990a) "East London Assessment Study".
7. Department of Transport (1990b) "South Circular Assessment Study".
8. Department of Transport (1990c) "South London Assessment Study".
9. Department of Transport (1990d) "West London Assessment Study".
10. Harris, N.G. (1989) "Capacity Restraint Simulation in a Public Transport Environment", *Traff. Engng. & Ctrl.* 30 pp. 312-315.
11. Harris, N.G. (1991) "Modelling Walk Link Congestion and the Prioritisation of Congestion Relief", *Traff. Engng. & Ctrl.* 32 pp. 78-80.
12. HMSO (1990) Transport Statistics Great Britain 1979-1989.

13. Maw, J.R. & Dix, M. (1990) "Appraisal of Station Congestion Relief Schemes on London Underground", Proc. PTRC Summer Annual Mtg, Univ. of Sussex pp. H167-178.
14. Miller, S.G., Vincent, J.F. & Wooltorton, G.A. (1990) "EMME/2: A New Generation in Software", *Trans. Plng. Systems* 1 pp. 21-32.
15. Mogridge, M.J.H. (1990) "Travel in Towns", Macmillan (308pp).
16. MVA (1990) LTS Version 2* Model Report.
17. Rickard, J.M. & Fearon, E.J. (1990) "Advances in Public Transport Assignment Modelling: Application of Proportional Assignment in Areas of Inner City Regeneration", Proc. PTRC Summer Annual Mtg, Univ. of Sussex pp. H179-190.
18. Wilson, M. (1990) Recent Developments in the Q-View Graphical Traffic Modelling Package", *Trans. Plng. Systems* 1 pp. 49-60.

10. The Management of Operations

Robert A Cochrane

Introduction

The operations management of many railway systems, including British Rail, is currently undergoing major changes in its responsibilities and organisation. In this chapter we briefly review the history of railway operations management in the United Kingdom, the organisational and technological factors which are responsible for the current changes and the management structures which are now emerging. This is a very broad subject, and it is impossible in a summary chapter of this nature to cover all its aspects. The intention is to provide an introduction together with a framework within which current developments in the operation of mixed traffic railways can be recognised and their origins understood.

The Historical Background

Mixed traffic railways have traditionally been managed on functional lines. Responsibility for the construction and maintenance of railway equipment has been in the hands of engineering functions, usually civil engineering, signalling and communications engineering, mechanical and electrical engineering. The planning and day-to-day operation of the railway services, including station operation, train operation and signal control, has been the responsibility of the operations function. In parallel with these activities a finance function has been responsible for central accounting and for the provision of cost control staff within the engineering and operations functions.

In the United Kingdom, this pattern of Regional management was inherited from the "Big Four" railway companies when the UK railway system was nationalised in 1947. It was strengthened by the adoption of similar functionally-based structures at Board Level for the original Railway Executive (1948-1953) and for the British Railways Board created in 1963[3].

A similar structure was used for the next tier of management below the Region, the Division, which was the level where day-to-day management of the Railway took place until its abolition in 1982-83.

This managerial framework remained essentially unaltered through several reorganisations so that in 1983 the British Railways Regions remained as shown in Figure 10.1.

Within a structure of this nature, the Regional Operations Manager was an extremely powerful figure with wide responsibilities. These covered train service planning, rolling stock scheduling, train running, on-board staffing, signal operation and the management and staffing of stations. The Regional General Manager had commercial managers responsible for marketing freight and passenger services reporting to him, but the railway was essentially production led.

The persistence of this management structure was in large measure a result of the influence of traditional railway technology and markets on railway economics. Sir William Ackworth[1] demonstrated, in an influential text first published in 1905, that on the mixed traffic railways of his time the majority of railway infrastructure costs were common or joint and the marginal cost of track maintenance decreased with traffic volume. He also pointed out that economies of scale could be obtained from corporate planning and joint use of locomotive power, since the number of locomotives required could be reduced by using them to

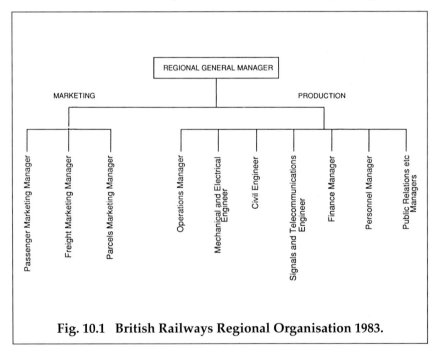

Fig. 10.1 British Railways Regional Organisation 1983.

haul different types of freight and passenger traffic at different times of day. He concluded that specific production costs could not be allocated to the provision of particular services in a meaningful way. This led him to advocate cost minimisation through corporate functional planning, allied with a policy of charging customers what the individual markets could bear.

Arguments of this nature provided a theoretical underpinning for the unified management of railway operations. As Gerry Fiennes said "He who produces the timetable manages the railway"[6]. The essence of railway management was unified and efficient operations management. The engineering functions supplied specialist skills and resources. These were coordinated by the operators through the development and operation of efficient timetables and locomotive, rolling stock and staff diagrams (working schedules) which minimised the total resources required.

The disadvantages of this functional organisation became increasingly apparent during the post war period. The functional structure was universal, and was carried down to a very low level within the railway. Individual maintenance depots, for example, were run by groups of staff with different functional reporting lines responsible for track and buildings, train movements and signalling and the maintenance and repair of the vehicles. This gave rise to a loss of management focus and accountability for the total cost of production activities requiring several functional inputs.

But it was the lack of any organisational or accounting link between revenue and cost which caused the greatest problems. Between 1960 and 1980 British Rail suffered major losses in important markets. Coal traffic for domestic use virtually disappeared and competition from road freight and the private car eroded traditional freight and passenger markets. Freight suffered particularly badly and national revenue from rail freight fell to less than half of the rail total for the first time in history in 1980. Stewart Joy[8] pointed out that much of the infrastructure required for freight was freight specific, and it was essential that freight traffic on a route should at least cover its specific infrastructure and its avoidable costs. But he recognised that such an apparently simple and logical rule was not easy to implement; neither the information required to make such decisions in a rational manner nor the management structure to drive them through was available. A management structure and internal accounting system was needed which would strengthen links between the supply of services and the costs incurred.

The solution which was adopted in 1983 was to introduce "Business Sectors" responsible on a national basis for each of the main areas of rail business. These business sectors (currently InterCity, Regional Railways, Network South East, European Passenger Services, Railfreight and Parcels) were given responsibility for the "net revenue" (income less attributed costs) which resulted from their business activities.

To support these businesses, a management accounting system was set up which exhausted specific, common and joint costs to the sectors using the "prime user" allocation concept, an approach designed to ensure that all rail assets and costs were underwritten by a business (for details see ref. 2). The basic responsibilities of the sectors were threefold. First, they provided marketing organisations for their business products and services. Secondly, they acted as internal buyers for production services within the railway through a complex three-dimensional matrix management system, described colloquially as "the Swiss Roll" or "the Rubik's Cube" depending on the graphical means used to illustrate it (Figure 10.2). Finally, they were responsible for business planning and hence the investment programme for the renewal of assets needed for their business operations.

The Impact of the UK Rail Businesses on Operational Management
Considerable scepticism was expressed at the time regarding both the advisability of a three-dimensional matrix structure and the likely impact of the Sector Directors on a production-led organisation over which they did not have traditional command and control authority. However, in retrospect there is no doubt that the sectors have brought about fundamental changes in railway management and that the three-way matrix provided the stepping stone needed by a conservative industry. The business directors have questioned the ability of current methods of operational management to maximise the net revenues accruing to each of their businesses. They have also looked outside Britain, and outside the railway industry, to see what technological changes are taking place which could benefit their individual businesses.

An example of the first type of pressure has been the concept of "dedication". Whereas conventional operations wisdom held that railway traction (i.e. locomotive) costs could best be minimised by joint working of locomotives between sectors to minimise locomotive numbers, businesses have preferred to own their own dedicated locomotive fleets, which they have modified to improve reliability and reduce maintenance costs when used in the specific type of duty demanded by their business requirements. Similarly, InterCity has preferred to use a separate dedicated group of guards, training them as

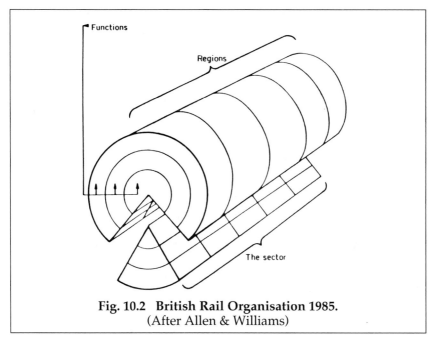

Fig. 10.2   British Rail Organisation 1985.
(After Allen & Williams)

Senior Conductors to provide customer services appropriate to their business needs as well as being responsible for the safety related duties of a guard.

The investment most closely associated with the individual businesses was rolling stock, and the sectors examined the technologies available at an early stage. They soon came to the conclusion that common technology was no longer an appropriate solution, and specialised rolling stock would prove more cost-effective. For example, Regional Railways recognised that the use of "cascaded" (i.e. second-hand) rolling stock previously operated by InterCity was not a cost-effective answer to their requirements and developed a range of purpose built diesel multiple units based on Dutch practice. Once its services were dependent only on Regional Railways' own specialised equipment, it was inevitable that the business would wish to take over responsibility for service specification and vehicle scheduling. Building on experience with the HST 125 (which divided the power required for high speed operation between two locomotives, one at each end of the set) InterCity moved towards the concept of the "unit train", a push-pull set which is not uncoupled in service and which avoids the need for locomotives to

109

run round or step back at terminal stations. This change has had major implications for methods of operation, locomotive scheduling, the level of vehicle reliability required, and the action to be taken if a vehicle becomes partially or totally unserviceable in traffic.

It also became apparent that the potential for benefits derived from specialised technology is not confined to rolling stock. Developments in very high speed railways, mass transit railway systems and light railways confirmed that significant benefits in operational efficiency and cost may be gained by the use of specialised track design and control systems which are tailored to the weight, speed and headway of the trains required to provide each type of service rather than accepting the limitations of a mixed traffic railway.

Changes in rail business requirements and the technologies available to support them have called into question both the traditional approach to railway operation and its economic underpinnings. Moreover, in the case of British Rail, the difficulties of operating within a three way management matrix have become more apparent as the influence and power of the businesses have increased. Such an organisation can only be transitional and it has become clear that simpler but more radical approaches to the structuring of operational management are needed.

Operational Management of Mixed Traffic Main Lines
Whilst new high speed, mass transit and light railways in Western Europe can benefit from the use of specialised vehicle technologies requiring a purpose designed and possibly dedicated track, the main line railway systems of the majority of countries (including the UK) are likely to continue to be mixed traffic railways, providing infrastructure for freight as well as local and long distance passenger services. Moreover, European national railway systems will be under increasing pressure from the European Commission to provide "open access" to international train service operators wishing to operate trains across national borders.

Fundamental to the analysis of mixed traffic railway operations is the definition of the geographical unit requiring a substantial degree of unified management. The basic management unit which has developed in response to the need to provide both fast, punctual long distance passenger services and local services on a common track is the line of route. A line of route is a railway route (such as the East Coast Main Line from London to Edinburgh and its associated spurs) which requires integrated train running control over its entire length to ensure reliable operation of the timetable. Line of route management is not an entirely new concept; Fiennes and Thorpe[5] gave a lot of thought to

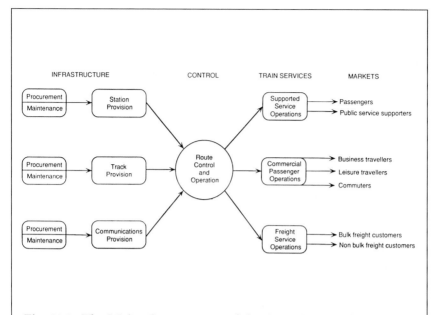

Fig. 10.3   The Major Components of the Organisational Structure.

"Line Management" on the Great Northern and Great Eastern Lines in the post war period, but they were still thinking in terms of unified management for all aspects of railway operation on the line. As the UK rail businesses have demonstrated, this may not be either necessary or desirable, and it is important to distinguish those core activities which must be under some form of unified management if a mixed railway is to operate reliably from those which are best provided by train operators serving the public.

To examine this question, we need to "unbundle" the railway organisation on a line of route into component activities in a way which demonstrates how they link together to support the service provided to the customer. Figure 10.3 shows these separate activities in a form similar to the "value chain" concept proposed by Michael Porter[9]. It could equally well be regarded as an update of Ackworth's theoretical separation of railway activities into "owning a road, supplying tractive power, owning the carrying stock and carrying for hire traffic of all sorts".

On the left hand side are shown the support activities associated with the provision of infrastructure. These support services are integrated

111

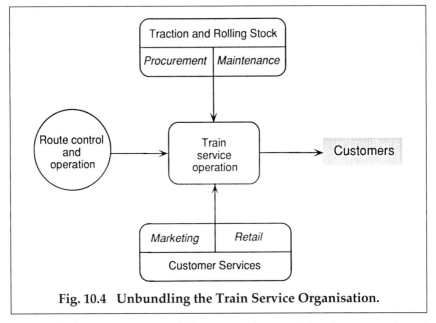

Fig. 10.4   Unbundling the Train Service Organisation.

through the route control function to provide the operational infrastructure on which the provision of train services depends. On the right hand side are shown the activities connected with the provision of train services serving the railway's markets. The train service organisation can itself be subdivided as shown in Figure 10.4; similar breakdowns could be provided for other activities.

The key feature from an operational point of view is the separation between the management of stations, the control of train running and the operation of the train services themselves. The most critical distinction is that between line control and train operation.

The specification of service requirements, the management of rolling stock and the provision of suitably skilled on-board staff are all closely related to serving specific market needs. Moreover, once trains and their crews are technically specialised and dedicated to different businesses, the advantages of corporate fleet and staff planning disappear. The management and running of train sets, together with their maintenance and staffing is best placed in the hands of train service operators.

Traditionally, the separation of line and train operating responsibilities would have been regarded as being likely to impair safety, but there has been a growing recognition that safe railway operation is not dependent on unified responsibility for operating safety. It depends on the clear documentation of operating and safety standards, the proper allocation of responsibility for specific safety related tasks (including safety monitoring and training) and the presence of clearly defined safety chains of responsibility leading up to the Managing Director responsible for each component business.

The activities which still need to be carried out in a unified manner on each line of route are those which are required to develop a unified timetable and control train running. The most important of these are the planning of major track maintenance and renewal, the construction of an overall timetable combining the needs of maintenance and the service requirements of all train operators using the route, the real time control of train operations and the provision of information on train running to the train service operators, both for their own management use and as a source of information for their customers.

This central role does not require ownership of major railway assets. Neither does it depend on the direct management of large numbers of staff. But both planning and real time control are heavily dependent on the ability to acquire and process information, which is itself dependent on the quality of the computer systems which support these activities. The current need is to improve these planning and operating systems.

Improved maintenance planning and timetable development systems would help to speed the process of timetable construction and increase the probability of subsequent reliable operation. Even greater advances are possible in the control of train running. Modern signalling systems relying on computer control and solid state interlocking are already taking the place of conventional power boxes. Signal control is likely to be centralised in a small number of centres, each controlling a hundred miles or so of track. Additional safety will be provided by automatic train protection systems which prevent trains passing signals at danger.

The major advance in real time control over the next ten years is likely to come from the introduction of higher level route control systems, which will provide information on the current status of all trains on the line of route (location, type, current minutes early or late, track status ahead). Such systems allow a central controller to make rational judgements on the running priority to be given to each train so as to achieve scheduled timings. Systems of this nature are already in use or on trial in a number of countries.

The Significance of Control in Railway Management
The role of line of route controller is the modern equivalent of that envisaged by Gerry Fiennes. "The man who coordinates the timetable

controls access to the route" does not have the same ring as his aphorism, but the basic power which is linked to the ownership of line control remains. It is for this reason that ownership of control has a major influence on the business structures possible for a modern railway, whether it is publicly or privately owned.

The close relationship between maintenance planning and timetable construction means that line of route control is probably best associated with management and maintenance of the infrastructure, though this approach has not been adopted in Sweden. Two basic forms of business organisation are possible on a line of route - the "business-led" and the "track company" structures. These are shown in Figure 10.5.

The track company model has been advocated by free market economists[4,10] and by the European Commission(EC). In this model ownership of the track and responsibility for line control are vested in a track company. Individual train companies can then operate services over the line, rather as express bus services might operate on a motorway. The difference, of course, is that a unified timetable has to be constructed incorporating the services each train company wishes to offer. This is difficult, but not impossible.

The advantage of the track company model is that the body responsible for control does not have a vested interest in the commercial success of a particular group of train services. The track company will wish to ensure open access to the line (the issue of greatest interest to the EC) and competition between train service operators. The disadvantage is that the track company is a monopoly supplier to all the train service operators. A high level of external monitoring and regulation of infrastructure maintenance and operating costs is likely to be needed.

The business-led model can be regarded as a rationalisation of British Rail's matrix structure and has been introduced in the United Kingdom over the last two years[7]. Similar organisation structures have been adopted in the United States for the operation of private railways. In this model, ownership of the track and control is vested in the train service operator who is responsible for the major long distance services operating over the line. In the United Kingdom, InterCity are the "lead business" on the main line routes; in the USA the lead business is normally a rail freight company. Secondary users of the line provide any additional infrastructure they require and operate their own train services under line control provided by the lead business.

This model provides vertical integration for the lead business, with the attendant advantages of greater control over track maintenance costs and easy coordination of major investment such as electrification.

It does, however, allow the lead business to exercise incumbency power, using its ownership of timetable planning and line control to restrict the ability of other train operators to compete with its own services.

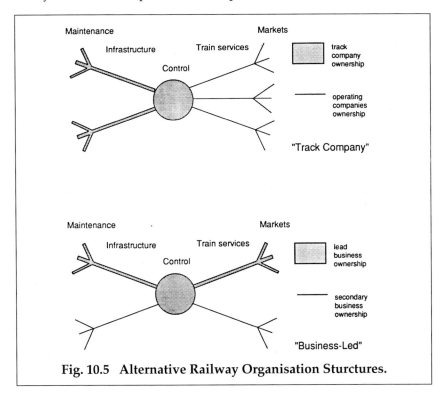

Fig. 10.5 Alternative Railway Organisation Sturctures.

Conclusion

The days of unified operational management on all but specialised single purpose railways have passed. In future, there is likely to be a clear distinction between operational duties associated with station management, line control and train service operation. Moreover, these separate responsibilities may well be undertaken by staff working for different businesses. But the power attached to the ownership of line control will remain. The issue which underlies the privatisation debate, the question of how to combine open access and on rail competition with efficient railway operation, is intimately bound up with the question as to who should be responsible for line control, and the degree of control which that body should possess.

115

References

1. Ackworth, Sir W. M. (1924), "The Elements of Railway Economics", 2nd Ed., O.U.P.
2. Allen, D. & Williams, G. (1985), "The Development of Management Information Systems to Meet the Needs of a New Management Structure for British Rail" in "International Railway Economics", eds. Button, K.J. & Pitfield, D.E., Gower.
3. Bonavia, M.R. (1971), "The Organisation of British Railways", Ian Allan.
4. Brittan, S. (1988), "A Restatement of Economic Liberalism", 1987-88 Edition, p. 253, MacMillan.
5. Fiennes, G.R. (1967), "I Tried to Run a Railway", Ian Allan.
6. Fiennes, G.R. (1986), "Themes on Rails", David and Charles.
7. Ford, R. (1991) "BR Reorganises on Business Lines", *Modern. Rlys.* 48 pp. 74-78.
8. Joy, S. (1971), "Pricing and Investment in Railway Freight Services", *Jnl. of Trans. Econ. and Pol.* 5, pp. 231-46.
9. Porter, M. (1985), "Competitive Advantage", Free Press.
10. Starkie, D. (1989), "British Rail: Competition on the Network" in "Privatisation & Competition", ed. Veljanovski, C., Institute of Economic Affairs.

Rail privatisation issues are discussed at length in Salveson, P. (1989) "British Rail: the Radical Alternative to Privatisation", Centre for Local Economic Strategies, Manchester, 158pp.

11. Signalling and Timetabling

Roger Ford and David Haydock

Basic Signalling

On the early railways, trains were controlled by hand-signals from railway policemen standing at the trackside. Time interval regulation was used. After a train had passed, the policeman would show the danger signal for 10 minutes, then a caution for a further five. This system failed to allow for a train which broke down just out of sight of a policeman. A second train arriving 15 minutes later would be given the all clear, only to run into the back of the failed train.

This problem was solved in the mid 1860s, with the introduction of the block telegraph. By now, there were signal-boxes at regular intervals dividing a line into 'blocks' and, with the electric telegraph, signalmen could now communicate with each other. Turning a switch deflected a needle in the next signal box along the line. Thus a signalman with a train in his block used the telegraph needle to indicate to the signalman in the next block along the line that a train was approaching. If the second signalman was sure that his block was clear, he telegraphed back, accepting the train.

Junctions were the other potential cause of collisions. Mechanical interlocking, which prevents the signal operator from setting up potential collisions, was in service by the mid 1850s. Points and signals were controlled by levers mounted in a frame. Moving the levers to set a route at a junction, locked any other levers in the frame which could be used to set a 'conflicting' route which would allow another train to enter the junction simultaneously.

Interlocking and block working remain the basics of railway signalling today[4]. However, almost all the vital functions are carried out electrically or, on the latest systems, electronically.

Electronic Signalling

A major reduction in the capital and operating costs of signalling has resulted from the development of electronic signalling where Britain has taken the lead. Today, signalling embraces a suite of computer control

117

systems and databases which provide the operator with a total overview of the railway.

In Solid State Interlocking (SSI) the safety logic is contained in the software run by three parallel microprocessors. Filing cabinet sized SSI cubicles replace large rooms full of electromagnetic relays. The interlockings communicate with trackside equipment over a multiplexed telecommunications system or 'data highway'.

SSIs generated multiple cost savings. First, the signal-box no longer has to accommodate a large relay room and can thus be smaller and cheaper. Second, manufacture of the previous electro-mechanical relays was labour intensive. Finally, relays have a finite life and require constant attention and replacement, where SSI is highly reliable and can be serviced by a single technician using replaceable electronics modules. Moreover, an important planning feature of SSI is that, unlike relay-based systems, the hardware is universal. The specific geographical information, such as track layout and signal positions, is in the software. Thus the signalling can be reconfigured very rapidly, simply by recompiling the software, in response to operational changes such as a new station layout. This is done at a special workstation.

Train Detection

Track circuits are used to detect the presence of a train in a block. Basically, an electric current is fed into one rail of each block. The steel wheels and axles of a train create a short circuit with the other rail which is used to indicate that the block is occupied.

However, modern track circuits are more than detection devices. 'Coded track circuits' can incorporate messages, in the form of coded frequencies, which can be picked by antennae on the train. For example, in Automatic Train Protection (ATP) systems, each frequency can represent a speed. The system can thus transmit to the train the maximum safe speed and the target speed at the end of the block section as determined by the signalling system.

Alternatively, the data can be transmitted by separate aerial loops beside the track or between the rails; in each case the information is processed by an on-board computer. In ATP systems, the on-board computer compares this data with the actual speed and makes an emergency brake application automatically if the train is about to exceed the maximum safe speed at any time, for example if the driver is not braking hard enough for a red signal.

Information

Train describers are computer databases which store the identity and

118

location of every train in the area of the control centre. This information can be compared with the timetable stored in another database. Comparison of the two by a computer allows the optimisation of operating strategies, for example automatic routing through junctions. Similarly, the train describer information can be used to drive passenger information systems without operator intervention.

These and associated systems come together in the Integrated Electronic Control Centre (IECC). Here, a small number of operators can control train services over a wide area using tracker balls to set routes on colour visual displays.

An important feature of the new electronic signalling and control technology is that it is less dependent on economies of scale than previous equipment. This is particularly valuable for lightly used passenger lines. For example, a single SSI interlocking cubicle can, using radio links with trackside equipment and trains, control extended single track train operation from a central control room. The saving on capital, maintenance and manpower costs can represent the difference between a line being closed and remaining open with a higher standard of service than before.

An Integrated System

In railway operation, it is not how fast a train can run which limits performance, but how well, and consistently, it can stop. As the signalling adage says, 'your power to stop is your right to speed'.

This becomes increasingly important as a service becomes more intensive. Block length, the spacing between signals, is determined by the braking distance of the vehicle. Consider the theoretical example of a railway line divided into blocks 500 m long to match the stopping distance of 50 km/h trains.

Assume that the line is signalled with colour lights which show red for danger and green for clear. A driver must be able to see the next signal from the start of a block if the train is to stop at a red aspect. For safety, there would have to be an empty block behind each train. Thus the theoretical minimum distance between trains running at line speed is two blocks = 1000 m which at 50 km/h gives a time interval between trains, known as the headway, of 1.2 min.

Because the energy to be dissipated in braking is proportional to the square of the speed, the stopping distance for a train travelling at 70 km/h will be 1,000 metres. If the railway is to run at this higher speed, signal spacings will have to be extended to 1000 metres. As a result, the distance between successive trains doubles and the time interval between trains becomes 1.7 minutes. Thus, increasing speed uses up

119

track capacity. To minimise this effect, the driver needs to be able to know what signal aspects are being displayed ahead. This facility is provided by multiple aspect signalling (MAS).

With MAS, the clear and danger signals are augmented by warning aspects. For example, a yellow aspect warns the driver that the next signal may be at red. This allows the driver to slow down to a speed at which he can stop safely when he sees the next signal. With this system, the 70 km/h train could run within the 500m signal spacing, providing that the drivers braked to 50 km/h when passing a yellow aspect.

In fact, the yellow aspect warns that the next signal is at red at that moment. However, if two trains are running together, the train in front will be clearing blocks as the train behind enters them. As a result, by the time that the second train reaches the next signal, it too may have changed to yellow. Thus the train behind is automatically regulated to the speed of the train in front.

Practical Timetabling

Traditionally, timetabling is done on a graph, with separate graphs for each route. Each graph is drawn to scale and shows stations, junctions and timing points with distances on the vertical scale. Time is shown on the horizontal scale with trains represented by lines running left to right and up or down depending on the direction of travel. On single track, these lines must cross at a passing loop (see figure 11.1). When lines representing trains travelling in the same direction cross, this means that a faster train is overtaking a slower one. The slower train must be "looped" - run into a passing loop to wait while the faster train passes. A stationary train is represented by a horizontal line.

Working out the timing of a train will depend on the projected maximum weight of the train and the type of motive power programmed for the train. These factors determine the point-to-point timings which will be known to the timetable planner. Timings for a train operating non-stop over a long distance will not be based on the maximum speed allowed by the line and train performance but somewhat below the maximum performance. A few minutes of "recovery time" is built into the timetable so that the driver can make up an unexpected delay or a speed restriction due to track works.

Traditionally, the fastest passenger trains are entered first on a blank graph, followed by local passenger trains with freight taking the "paths" which remain. (A path is a straight line through the traffic graph for a certain type of train which translates on the real track as a clear run for the train). This situation may now be changing as freight customers become more demanding about timings. Except when a line

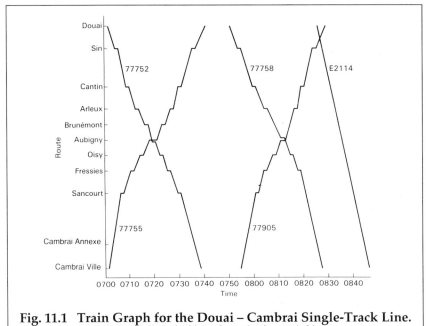

Fig. 11.1 Train Graph for the Douai – Cambrai Single-Track Line.
N.B. Douai-Sin is double track; passing loop at Aubigny.

is totally saturated, a timetable planner will always plan a number of paths between regular trains in order to cater for extra trains due to unexpected demand, for example, relief passenger trains in holiday seasons or "conditional" freight trains. Note that "drawing" the graph is now often done on a computer screen.

The reduction in track capacity caused when trains of varied speeds are mixed can be demonstrated on a graph. Figure 11.2 is a theoretical graph for a line between A and B which are separated by 50 kilometres, with no passing loops. In Fig. 11.2a, expresses operating at 100km/h average are traced every 6 minutes. There are, thus, 6 departures between 1000 and 1030. In Figure 11.2b, an express at 1000 is followed by a freight, traced at 50km/h average. The next express departure from A is now not possible until 1042, given 6 minute spacing between trains.

Figure 11.3 shows passenger trains between Arras and Seclin (in France) during the 0800 to 0900 period (two possible freight paths at 60km/h average are shown in dotted lines). Note that expresses R35, R2203 and E2505 are "flighted" together, leaving Arras at 0826, 0829 and 0833 respectively, R 35 having overtaken R2203 at Arras. Flighting

121

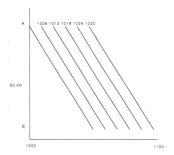

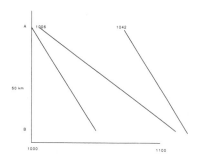

Fig. 11.2 a
Train Graphs for Trains of Equal
Performance.

Fig. 11.2 b
Train Graphs for Trains of
Different Performance.

means grouping fast trains together in order to leave time for slower trains to pass before being caught up by other fast trains.

Timetabling the trains is, however, only part of the overall timetabling process. "Rosters" of work for locomotives, rolling stock and staff all need to be drawn up, and some vehicles may be dedicated to particular types of work, whilst others are pooled between various duties. An iterative process may need to be followed if the preferred timetable is inefficient in its use of resources, since the aim is to provide the maximum service with the fewest resources; some slight alteration to the timetable may permit a complete train to be spared, with its work being covered by others in marginal time. This is critical in keeping costs down (see chapter 17).

Timetabling for the Passenger Market
It is possible to identify two main philosophies of timetable planning for the passenger market. The first consists of trying to provide passenger carrying capacity exactly when and where detailed market research shows it is needed, maximising seat occupation as far as possible. We can call this the "market-led" approach. The second involves providing a "regular interval timetable" which maximises frequency and regularity. Although this approach has clear advantages (for instance, "clockface" departures are easily remembered by passengers and staff), it may force the passenger to adapt to train times which may not suit him/her well. This is a "production-led" approach. Regular interval timetables may concern a restricted number of lines or, as is increasingly common, the complete national railway network.

122

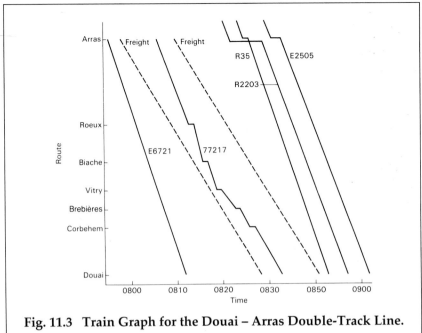

Fig. 11.3 Train Graph for the Douai – Arras Double-Track Line.

The Market-led Approach

Take a simplified example of a market-led timetabling process - a railway operator identifies a market of, say, 4,000 passengers per day (in one direction) between cities A and B, and decides to run 10 trains a day, with each train having seating capacity for 500 passengers, this would represent an average seat occupation of 80%. Given the variation in loading which can occur between trains from day to day, 80% is probably too high - SNCF is satisfied with an average of around 70% on its TGV services. Once it has been decided to run 10 trains a day, each train must be placed at the optimum departure/arrival time. In most cases, Monday-Friday, this means finding arrival times in B which suit business passengers during the 0700-1000 period and convenient departure times from a between 1600 and 1800. As with the problem of finding optimum "slots" for take-off and landing at airports, this may not be very easy as station platform space at A and B will be at a premium during these peak periods and trains on other lines will be "competing" for these same "slots". Outside these peaks, the timetable planner also has to juggle with the preferences and numbers of different

123

types of passengers using the trains and with the variations in passenger numbers on different days of the week.

The timetable planner will try to run a train from A to B at the maximum commercial speed possible in order to compete with other modes. If there are no stations of importance between A and B, operation will be non-stop. However, if a large town, C, lies between the two, with a potential market of 400 passengers a day each way to both A and B, the planner must decide on how many A-B trains to stop at C in order to cater for the demand there, without unduly penalising A-B travellers.

SNCF is the leading exponent of tailoring the timetable exactly to the travel market. Many of its trains have variations on Friday, Saturday, Sunday and Monday with only Tuesday to Thursday having the same service. One could argue that this takes the approach to extremes and leads to a timetable which is difficult to understand by staff let alone the travelling public. The travel agents Thomas Cook, who edit their own timetables, claim that the SNCF Paris-Cherbourg service is the most complicated in the world!

Within the urban environment, the slow speed of trains in signalling blocks containing stations can cause pathing problems if the service is intensive (when the line is said to be at or near capacity). A possible approach (if the majority of passengers wish to access one main station) is that of "skip-stopping", where alternate trains stop at alternate stations, but this gives no service between local stations, which is usually unacceptable, so "all-stations" services also have to be run. As a result, most metro operators run all-stations services, and merely ensure that the signalling is adequate.

The Production-led Approach: Regular Interval Timetables

Once traffic on a line reaches a level where more than 10-15 trains, spread throughout the day, are justified, the timetable planner may decide to operate the service with a regular stopping pattern at a regular hourly interval; this is known as a clock-face or regular interval timetable (RIT). A standard service frequency has the advantage for the passenger of being easily remembered. This, plus the knowledge that there is always "another one behind" after only one hour, in the case of missing a chosen train, is comforting to the passenger and may be a positive factor in the choice of the rail mode. (Conversely, a confusing timetable with many long periods between trains, may discourage the potential user).

RIT's have been common throughout Europe for many years, particularly on intensive suburban services, but less so on Inter City routes. German Federal Railways (DB) introduced a coordinated network of regular interval expresses in 1971, which were First Class only and generally at two-hour intervals. The First Class market proved too small to maintain such regular trains on all four Inter City (IC) routes. On the other hand, the German Second-Class market was badly served by trains averaging only 80km/h and covering only 82% of costs. A new IC network was introduced in 1979 with fast hourly two-class services on four routes[1]. For Second Class passengers, speeds were raised to 103km/h average whilst First Class customers saw their service doubled in frequency.

One notable feature of this IC network is the arrangement for direct connections at the key interchanges of Hannover, Dortmund, Köln, Frankfurt, Mannheim and Wurzburg. In the absence of services, interchange between IC trains each hour is made as simple as possible. Trains are formed of the same number of coaches in the same formation and received on adjacent platforms. Thus an interchanging passenger simply crosses the platform to find the equivalent accommodation on his onward train. In 1991, the German IC network comprises six routes, with ICE high-speed trains operating one route and two-hourly InterRegio (IR) services completing the long-distance network[6]. Further extensions are likely in future as former East Germany is gradually incorporated in the national plan.

RIT at a National Level

Nederlandse Spoorwegen (NS) were European pioneers in operating a completely integrated RIT. As early as 1970, services throughout Holland were recast on hourly or better frequencies with easy cross-platform connections at important stations.

The Swiss "Taktfahrplan", first planned in 1973, proposed three types of services, (InterCity, semifast and local all-station stopping trains), with all trains generally hourly. In planning the timing of trains, particular attention was paid to maintaining good connections. As Swiss railways are heavily trafficked by freight trains, it was necessary to "flight" passenger trains in many cases. In order to produce consistent performance, trains of the same category on the same route generally have the same weight and motive power.

Taktfahrplan involved a significant increase in train frequencies. In the InterCity category, the number of potentially-popular high-quality trains on each route rose from 5 - 10 to around 15 trains per day. Train kilometres increased by 56%. Costs did not rise by the same amount as the new services were largely possible using existing staff and rolling stock more productively. SBB did not try to predict accurately increased ridership and revenue; the project was very much product-led. The SBB were able to cite the experience of certain service improvements on specific lines, including the introduction of regular interval services which had produced patronage increases of up to 30% in one year.

Swiss Taktfahrplan was finally introduced in 1982. Whilst it did not produce large increases in rail use, the SBB and Swiss Federal Government considered it to be a success because it prevented further passenger traffic losses. SBB now has a plan known as "Bahn 2000" to upgrade the hourly Taktfahrplan[2]. Where necessary this will be done by increasing line speeds but, interestingly, higher speeds are considered subservient to "convenience" (frequency and connections) in certain cases. Acceleration increases track maintenance costs and reduces track capacity.

Belgian Railways (SNCB) introduced their RIT in 1984. Unlike the Swiss case, the background was more one of contraction and economies, with 150 stations and 160 kilometres of line closed. The change to even interval working and reduction of intermediate stops brought an improved service for passengers. Based around two main levels of service – InterCity (IC) and InterRegional (IR) – it allowed SNCB to increase the productivity of rolling stock and staff. Regular interval services had been common in Belgium before 1984. In 1935 they were a feature of the electrified Brussels - Antwerpen service, but the 1984 changes were the first to consider the network as a whole with planned connections throughout the system. Although passenger traffic continued on a downward trend in 1984, an upturn of 2% was recorded in 1985, the first full year of the RIT. Receipts rose by 8%. Overall, IC-IR is considered a success which SNCB wishes to build on. In its current long term plan, STAR 21, SNCB plans to introduce an improved level of service to the RIT, with better rolling stock and faster services, known as InterCity Plus.

The latest convert to RIT is Austrian Federal Railways (ÖBB). In June 1991 they inaugurated their "NAT 91" (Neue Austro-Takt) network[3]. This consists of seven principal routes, operated at two-hourly frequencies, with connections at main interchange stations. Train kilometres were increased by over a quarter and by over 41% for the fastest trains (Schnellzüge). The 1991 measures are the first in a plan to accelerate Austria's trains significantly through selective line upgrading and the introduction of tilting trains in 1993.

Problems of Regular Interval Timetables
Although RIT's bring many advantages for the passenger, they impose certain restrictions on the operator. Once in place, it is difficult to make

even minor alterations to one service without creating a cascade of changes to other services. Thus, the timetable is "set in stone" for many years. In addition, the timetable chosen may not exactly correspond to the needs of certain types of passenger. Journeys for leisure purposes are not usually "time sensitive" and a well constructed timetable with easy connections may attract more of this traffic. In the case of business or education, an arrival or departure within 15 minutes of a fixed time is usually desired.

SNCB discovered this problem when they introduced their IC-IR timetable in 1984. In post introduction surveys, commuters were the least satisfied group. More seriously, badly timed trains brought children and students to school or college 5 minutes too late or left a short time before the children could arrive at the station. As a result of protests, SNCB laid on extra peak trains, whilst leaving the RIT intact.

Another major problem is that of track maintenance. European railways who do not operate a regular interval timetable usually programme periods of the day for work on the track. SNCF try to free between 1.5 and 2 hours per day when there are no trains, typically 09:30 to 12:00 or 14:00 to 16:00. Clearly an RIT makes this impossible. In Switzerland, the introduction of Taktfahrplan led to a revision of maintenance practice. Previously, some fairly long intervals existed between trains, allowing ample time for routine maintenance. With Taktfahrplan, the longer periods were replaced with shorter but more regular periods. The problem can also be eased by the simple but expensive measure of signalling double track for reversible working.

British Rail differs from mainland European countries in programming a significant amount of its track maintenance between Saturday night and Sunday afternoon. This results in an extremely reduced service with increased journey times on Sunday morning. In contrast, mainland European railways operate an almost normal weekend service. On the SNCF's high speed lines, maintenance is normally carried out at night.

Dissemination of Timetable Information

Timetable information has traditionally been sold in book form. Railways usually sell timetable books in station kiosks or at ticket and information offices. In most cases these are sold at around cost price.

For those passengers who only use one service or group of services regularly, most railways produce free leaflets or booklets which are available in the stations concerned. In other cases, the information is edited by the local authority with the aim of promoting public transport. In the latter case other modes of transport may be included and thus integration may be promoted.

Deutsches Bundesbahn (DB), the German Federal Railway also make free leaflets available in long distance trains. These "Zugbegleiter" (train courier) give timings for each station stop, with a list of onward connections at each station. These leaflets are financed by advertising.

Giving timetable and other passenger train information by telephone has been rationalised by most railway authorities. Rather than each station giving information for its services, calls are channelled to a regional information centre. This allows a multiplication of lines with a call queuing system and avoids the duplication of information equipment. Recorded messages with restricted information about a particular or set of services are used by some railways including BR and DB.

Computers

In the late 1980's computers started to come into their own for train information. DB used self service terminals on station concourses to disseminate information to passengers. A potential passenger would type in his destination and the terminal would produce a list of trains in the following hours.

BR introduced their "Computer Assisted Timetable Enquiry" - CATE system in 1990. This system, which reads out all trains from any station to any other, including interchange times, is only used by station staff. DB has developed a similar system called "EVA" for use by information staff at large stations. The SBB also has a system which prints a sheet giving personalised journey information.

SNCF are by far the most advanced in their use of computers. They were one of the first railways to develop programs which gave staff information on trains between two stations via the optimum route. Given the travelling customer's difficulty in using paper-based timetables, SNCF decided to make their computer-based timetable accessible to the public at an early stage. In France, telephone subscribers can request a free visual terminal, the MINITEL. This offers a very large range of Teletext-style information services via the telephone line. SNCF made its timetables available on Minitel from 1985.

The Minitel service has gradually been upgraded and at present a customer can access a list of trains between any two points including those where a change is necessary. The customer can then reserve a place on a chosen train collecting his reservation and ticket from a station later. To avoid a special journey the customer can send the payment to SNCF and receive the ticket by post. SNCF is now experimenting with payment by credit card through a terminal connected to the Minitel although this service is restricted so far to companies.

The Nederlandse Spoorwegen (NS) introduced a further innovation in timetable dissemination in the summer of 1990. NS made a diskette (for IBM and compatible computers) containing complete timetable details for Holland available to the public. Users consult a network map then input their origin and destination stations followed by limits on departure and arrival times. After a maximum 90 second search the program outputs the optimum trains corresponding to the request. Interchange times plus alternative routes and a choice of fares are also displayed. It must be stressed that this approach is only possible as Holland is a small country with a simple regular interval timetable. Only a few international and peak hour trains fall outside the repetitive hourly pattern of services throughout the day.

References

1. Cooper B.K. (1979) "Every Hour - Each Class: DB's Two - class Inter City Network", *Modern Rlys.* 36 pp. 494 - 497.
2. Freeman Allen G. (1986) "Bahn 2000 - Switzerland's New National Passenger Rail Plan", *Modern Rlys.* 43 pp. 129 - 133.
3. Freeman Allen G. (1991). "Austria's £3 billion New Railway Takes Shape", *Modern Rlys.* 48 pp. 21 - 29.
4. Kichenside, G.M. and Williams, A. (1978). British Railway Signalling, 4th edn., Ian Allan.
5. Perren, B. (1973) "Taktfahrplan Schweiz", *Modern Rlys.* 30 pp. 308-311 and 350-353.
6. Perren, B. (1991) "DB Launches InterCity Expresses (ICE)", *Rail* 152 (July10-23) p.40.
7. 'Velocior' (1991) "Timetabling Freight Trains", *Modern Rlys.* 48 pp. 141-142.

12. Punctuality and Performance

Nigel G Harris

Introduction

Most public transport planning takes account of the basic attributes of a public transport journey, namely its monetary cost and its duration (as we have seen in chapter 1). However, if passengers are questioned as to the elements of the service which are most important to them in their mode choice decision, other service characteristics (which it is difficult to include in a generalised cost framework) are also often mentioned e.g. the comfort of the seats, reliability (see ref. 2 in respect of stage bus services) and even the scenic nature of the route[5]. One of the reasons for the infeasibility of including some of these variables is that, in the past, it has not been possible to predict them for a given journey, even in a probabilistic fashion; there has been no research and, often, not even any data collection.

This is important since, for some passengers, such factors as punctuality are critical; the provision of a reliable arrival time may outweigh the prospect of a faster journey but with a less certain arrival time. Moreover, punctuality is perceived to be worse than it actually is, for three reasons:

(i)   passengers have a degree of selective memory, tending to remember poor performances at the expense of good ones;
(ii) more passengers travel on late trains than on punctual ones (because late trains follow longer-than-average gaps in the service); and
(iii) operators avoid early running, so that very late arrivals are not generally balanced out by very early arrivals.

Murray[9] has also suggested that passengers expect railways to run to time (unlike airlines and buses) because the railway operator is considered to be in greater control of his/her own environment.

Reliability is not only of concern to passengers, but to operators as well. Knowledge of punctuality and how passengers respond to it helps operators in their decisions as to the cost-effectiveness of using more rolling stock to improve punctuality and attract passengers, or of lowering fares to achieve the same end. In the short term, an improved understanding of reliability enables operators to determine the most efficient workloads for both rolling stock and traincrew; in the longer term, it enables them to determine more accurately the optimum levels of investment in resources (rolling stock, traincrew and physical infrastructure). For example, in the mid 1980s, BR's Southern Region installed an additional passing loop at Tisbury (in Wiltshire), solely with the aim of improving punctuality on a single-track line renowned for its poor operational performance. However, as Wilson[12] has asked, how does one justify expenditure on expensive extra capacity if all it does is to increase reliability? This question has been answered by Cochrane[4], who set out how BR's InterCity sector traded off passengers' perceived costs of arriving late against journey time elasticities; the result of that trade-off was a business decision to aim for 90% of arrivals within 10 minutes.

Punctuality is, of course, dependent upon a particular published timetable, and can therefore be readily manipulated by the operator. However, merely slackening schedules by including more "recovery time", so that a greater proportion of trains arrive at the booked time, may be an extremely inefficient way of improving performance. Trains may arrive early, but have to wait time for continuing their journey or beginning their next one, so resources may not be well-used. Such timetable manipulation also does not affect the tendency of certain services to become late, which is the focus of this chapter.

Punctuality Research: Data Collection
The research reported here, the initial results of which were set out by Rodley and Harris[10], marks the first step into gaining a better understanding of railway reliability, by comparing the actual punctuality of services with advertised times. Anglian[1] also set out the kinds of incidents which cause problems of poor punctuality; note that 5% of them are due to factors outside the railway's sphere of influence (such as vandalism and the weather (see Fig. 12.1)).

From such data, we can hypothesise a number of underlying variables which are thought to affect the punctuality of trains:
1. Length of train in carriages: affects the time taken to traverse and accelerate away from additional stops, speed restrictions etc; more doors to be left open (or to malfunction if automatic door stock).
2. Previous number of station stops: a potential cause of lateness through loading and unloading passengers and parcels, waiting for connections etc. Under-powered services also fare worse on routes with more stops and therefore more required acceleration.

131

3. Previous distance covered: the likelihood of encountering either vandalism or track defects increases with increasing distance traversed.
4. Age of the motive power unit: rolling stock failures follow the 'bath-tub' curve (see chapter 21); after a spate of initial failures, most trains run well for 20 years or so before becoming increasingly unreliable.
5. Track occupation: The busier a railway is, the more likely it is that one failure will cause problems for other services. This variable was estimated, for multiple track lines, into three categories of (a) a train in the preceding 15.01 minutes; (b) a train in the preceding 15.01-30.01 minutes, and (c) no preceding train within 30 minutes. For single track lines, these headways were multiplied by two.

Fig. 12.1   Adverse Weather affects punctuality: EMU at Colchester running 30 minutes late during snowy weather.

Results were also analysed by the operator responsible (BR's three business sectors or Netherlands Railways (NS)), since they run quite different types of services, and results would be expected to be different.

Research Method

The basic technique used was least-squares Multiple Linear Regression (MLR), with punctuality as the dependent variable. For a small number of trains, which had been travelled on on more than 30 occasions, longitudinal data sets were available, which gave an indication of the usual spread of arrival times of one train.

However, it was important to know whether or not the variation in performance of the whole data-set available here was significantly different from the variation in punctuality exhibited by the six samples. For this, the F test and a 5% confidence limit was used, where:

$$F = \frac{T\,\dfrac{s_y^2}{}}{s^2} = \frac{\text{explained variation}}{\text{unexplained variation}}$$

where T = no. of points per sample (approx. 40)

s^2 = average variance of samples

s_y^2 = variance of the sample means[13].

This gave an F statistic of 1.87, more than the critical point of 1.51, indicating that it was unlikely that the samples and whole data-set were statistically-similar. The randomness of each train's performance is thus shown to be relatively small compared to the variation within the whole data-set, which was then used for cross-sectional analysis using multiple regression.

Multiple Regression Analysis

Fig. 12.2 and Table 12.1 show that the problem is indeed one worth investigating - the mean lateness for the entire sample of 4342 trains was nearly three minutes, within which the latest (-170 minutes) more than made up for the earliest (+21 minutes). If BR carry 746M passengers p.a.[3], and trains average 2.81 minutes late, then the total delay is nearly 400 person-years - a considerable disbenefit to the country and its economy.

The figures in Table 12.1 immediately scotch one common misconception viz. that British Rail is systematically more late than its Continental counterparts. Although the Dutch sample is small, it is nevertheless statistically-significant, and the lateness it indicates shows a performance worse than that of NSE, which is a comparable system. The author suggests that this misconception is a function not necessarily of ignorance (although this may play a part) but rather of journey purpose; British people use BR for work and business journeys (when they have a high Value of Time, so punctuality is important to them) but foreign railways only for leisure purposes (e.g. when on holiday), when they are less time-sensitive.

Sector	Mean Punctuality (mins)	Standard Dev. (mins)	Sample Size
InterCity	-5.45	15.66	691
Network SouthEast	-1.93	6.25	2046
Regional	-2.81	9.24	1572
Dutch	-2.18	4.74	33
ALL	-2.81	9.49	4342

Table 12.1. Mean and Standard Deviation of Punctuality by Operating Sector.

The second stage of MLR is to build up a correlation matrix, since results can be affected by significant correlation between the independent variables. In fact, although STOPS and MILES were significantly correlated, the two variables never appear in the same equation, since once any variability has been explained by MILES, there is little left for STOPS. Punctuality of the whole data-set is shown to be correlated with STOPS, MILES and LENGTH, also true for the Regional subset, but the InterCity subset does not show a correlation between punctuality and the number of stops, whilst the NSE and Dutch datasets do not show any significant correlations involving punctuality.

Table 12.2 shows the results of the regression. Only two of the independent variables (miles covered and train length) are statistically-significant in determining punctuality. Of greater interest, perhaps, is that miles is the governing variable in the longer-distance regimes of InterCity and Regional railways, whilst train length (partly proxying for passenger demand) is the critical variable for NSE and Dutch railways.

As can be seen, whilst T statistics are high, R^2 values are low; this does not necessarily constitute a contradiction. There is considerable random variation (or at least, variation caused by a large number of factors operating only occasionally), as is shown by Fig. 12.2; for any value of any given independent variable, there will be a considerable range of likely delays. A robust timetable (one where slight delays do not generate longer delays because 'paths' across junctions are too slim) is therefore important for all but the least-used infrastructure. However, the high T statistics confirm the general relationship with a great degree of certainty, as is shown in Fig. 12.3.

134

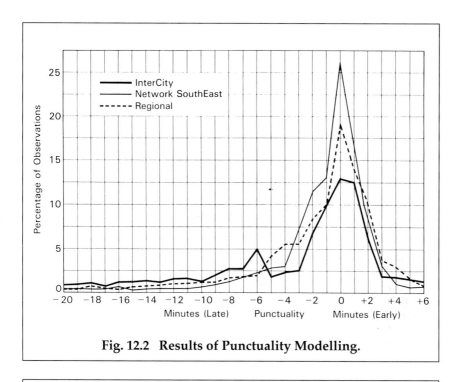

Fig. 12.2 Results of Punctuality Modelling.

Sector	R²	F	Variable	b	T	Constant	T
InterCity	.05731	41.886	MILES	-.0284	-6.47	-1.0945	-1.232
		(.0000)			(.0000)		(.2183)
Network SE	.01764	36.699	LENGTH	-.31082	-6.06	-.6222	.175
		(.0000)			(.0000)		(.8612)
Regional	.05822	97.056	MILES	-.0337	-9.85	-.9852	-3.371
		(.0000)			(.0000)		(.0008)
Dutch	.21091	8.286	LENGTH	-1.3593	-2.878	2.6787	1.452
		(.0072)			(.0072)		(.1567)
ALL	.06120	141.44	MILES	-.02683	-14.664		
		(.0000)			(.0000)		
			LENGTH	-.12731	-2.353	-.4824	-1.462
					(.0187)		(.1438)

(Values in brackets are t statistics).

Table 12.2 Punctuality Distributions.

135

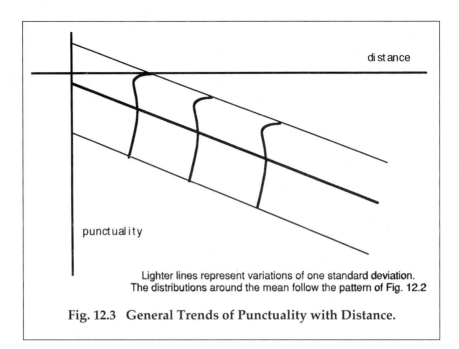

Fig. 12.3   General Trends of Punctuality with Distance.

Implications for Operators of Short-Distance Services

The results of the regression force us to consider implications by type of railway operation; demand management is the key for urban operations. With train length the determinant, the passenger interface at stations, with large numbers of boardings and alighting along the length of the train, is critical; the service will no longer run itself. Particular attention will need to be paid to driver skill, whilst station staff may be required in numbers to get trains away on time. At high service frequencies, junction problems also occur, whilst trains also tend to bunch in conditions of heavy demand following a cancellation or late train. Where these problems are particularly serious (e.g. on underground rail lines), great attention needs to be paid, as there can be safety management problems if passenger numbers build up on platforms or, indeed, on trains. London Underground (for example) has considerable overcrowding in the peak hours (and at some other times too), and has developed a sophisticated Train Service Model[11]. Modelling of great detail (such as the exact doorway widths on rolling stock) may be critical if crush loading of rolling stock and/or running frequencies close to the signalled headway are envisaged.

Note also that additional problems arise when the service frequency approaches that of the signalled capacity, since any delay means that subsequent trains have to be late, since they are prevented by the signalling system from making up time. Thus some trains at the end of the peak can become offpeak services as they queue for a path through a congested track section. "Turnback" sidings may be useful before the end of the line if services become delayed; although use of them reduces the service offered to the last few stations on the line, it can significantly improve punctuality in the reverse direction, by feeding trains back into the system on schedule.

Implications for Operators of Long-Distance Services
The issues here are quite different from those outlined above; the factors causing long-distance timetables to degrade are those variables which can recur throughout the journey e.g. engineering works, number of junction and single-line conflicts, proneness to vandalism and severe weather. These must be taken into consideration when through-running of services is considered. BR's Regional railways sector has recently developed an Express network of services connecting (for example) East Anglia with the North-West of England, partly on the basis that through-running a string of previously-independent local services reduces inefficient layover times in termini. However, we can see here that terminal layover times (which can be used to reduce delays of incoming services) cannot be dispensed with, even for through services. The recovery times explained in chapter 11 apply nonetheless to through services, and need to be maintained before the same major stations which used to be termini; for longer-distance services, additional time may be needed to prevent unsatisfactory punctuality levels occurring, because of the potential knock-on effects of transmitting slightly-late running to the next major interchange station. Moreover, higher speeds increase unreliability because trains require more time to recover from unscheduled stops.

Nevertheless, because we can derive the standard deviation of punctuality in the different environments studied, we can make recommendations as to the levels of recovery time required if management set out their standards (e.g. 95% of trains to arrive within 10 minutes of the booked time). For example, assuming that early-running trains are held to await time, and an otherwise-normal distribution of punctuality, then allowing a margin at junctions of only 1 standard deviation would leave 15.87% of trains to suffer the possibility of further delay, which is unacceptable in terms of the hypothetical target set (see Table IV of ref. 13). However, Table 12.1 shows that even this 1 s.d. margin means up to 15 minutes between conflicting moves - and this excludes the additional delay through having to stop and subsequently restart and accelerate a train which may be travelling at 125mph and having a braking distance of over a mile (Note that, the lower the line-speed, the less significant this latter factor). As through-running is thought to increase the standard deviation, we can see that it should therefore be accompanied by increases in recovery time greater than those simply implied by the additional distance traversed.

Track Layouts and Operational Performance
The punctuality distributions of Fig. 12.2 show how problems may arise if the distributions of trains with potentially-conflicting train movements interact (see Fig. 12.4). Clearly, adopting the standard deviation approach in isolation would cause unnecessary difficulties in timetabling any but the sparsest service, which is why good timetables involve particular 'moves' being made together - e.g. trains to and from the Caerphilly and Pontypridd corridors are timetabled to pass at Cardiff Queen Street (see Fig. 12.5a); they are also flighted, to maximise the length of the paths available for conflicting movements - see chapter 11 for a further discussion of this. On Southern Region's network of suburban services on London and Surrey, however, the service is so complicated that these elements of good timetabling cannot always be achieved; this might in itself be a good reason for service simplification (see ref. 7) but of course, the demand impacts of such changes would also have be taken into consideration.

Junction design is of itself important in determining the capacity of the railway. 'Double junctions' used to be installed as standard at the meeting of two double-track lines, but permanent way engineers have argued recently that these are difficult to maintain, and they have preferred 'ladder junctions' (see Fig. 12.5b). Although these do not permit parallel moves, they may contain standard (and therefore cheaper) pointwork, and recent accidents at Westerton and Newton have questioned their safety. They also allow for transfer between tracks which is usually needed as an additional element of the trackwork found at double junction locations. Such crossovers are usually required anyway, at distances ranging between 3 miles (for underground systems) and 10 miles (for InterCity routes) in order to facilitate the transfer of trains between tracks for engineering or diversionary purposes.

Punctuality is also critically affected by the number of tracks available because line capacity increases more quickly than the number of tracks. On adding a second track, unidirectional operation is possible, which

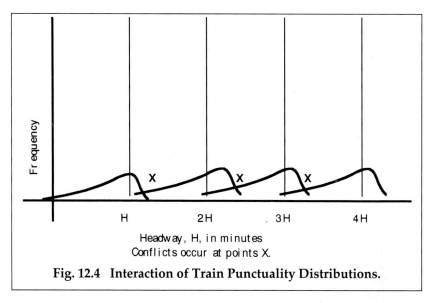

Headway, H, in minutes
Conflicts occur at points X.

Fig. 12.4   Interaction of Train Punctuality Distributions.

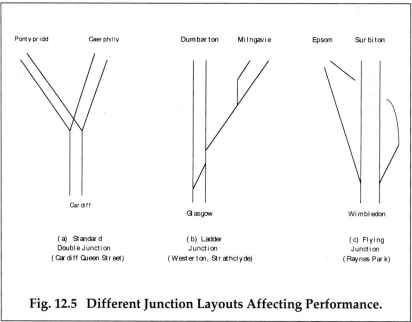

Fig. 12.5   Different Junction Layouts Affecting Performance.

reduces the wasted time waiting for on trains to traverse single-line sections. Four-track operation, as opposed to that over two tracks, has substantial advantages in that one pair of tracks can be used for fast services, and the other for slow and freight; the loss of capacity associated with running services of mixed speeds is substantial, as has already been shown in chapter 8. However, demand must indeed be heavy for four tracks to be required, as modern signalling systems can cope with 30 or more suburban passenger trains per hour per track.

Where four tracks are in place, however, decisions need to be taken as to how they are arranged, there being two sensible formations. In the first, the fast and slow lines are paired (as between Paddington and Reading); in the second, the fast lines are together in the middle of the formation, with their respective slow lines outside them (e.g. between King's Cross and Stevenage). This latter arrangement allows for the ready switching of trains between fast and slow lines, but has the disadvantage that, at terminals, slow trains may need to cross all the fast lines in order to gain access to or from a suitable platform. In a number of locations, flyovers (e.g. at Holloway) or burrowing junctions (see Fig. 12.6) have been constructed to do this without impairing the performance of the main lines. Moreover, access to branch lines will be a problem for those trains needing to cross the fast lines, and flying junctions may be required, either constructed as flyovers or underpasses (see Fig. 12.5c). Perhaps the line with the most of these is the Waterloo - Southampton main line; during the 1930s, the LSWR went to considerable expense to build flying junctions along this line (at Raynes Park, New Malden, Surbiton (2), Brookwood and Basingstoke) since demand was rising sufficiently to create more train movements than could be catered for with flat junctions. In more modern times, extension of the Docklands Light Railway to Beckton has necessitated construction of flying junctions near Poplar[8].

Further detail on railway permanent way may be found in Coster[6].

Conclusions
Train delays are due to a wide range of factors, but amongst these, the distance covered and the length of the train in carriages are important to long- and short-distance services respectively. This means that the appropriate management response for each environment is in terms of ensuring sufficient recovery time for long-distance services, but in terms of demand management for short-distance services. Track layouts can be critical in determining the operational performance of any service.

Fig. 12.6   Double and Burrowing Junctions in the Inner
Suburbs of München.

References

1. Anglian (1989) "BR Wishes to Apologise...", *Modern Rlys.* 46 pp. 461-464.
2. Bly, P.H. (1976) "Depleted Bus Services: the Effect of Rescheduling", TRRL LR 699.
3. BRB (1990) "Annual Report and Accounts 1989-1990".
4. Cochrane, R.A. (1989) "A Business-Led Basis for InterCity Punctuality Standards", paper presented to the Transport Statistics Users' Group Conference, London.
5. Cook, H. & Pope, J. (1982) "Attitudes and Beliefs of Rail and Non-Rail Users to Modal Choice Between Exmouth and Exeter", Plymouth Polytechnic, Department of Shipping and Transport Working Paper 5.
6. Coster, P.J. (1981) "Permanent Way", ch. 3 pp. 21-35 in Cooper, B.K. "British Rail Handbook".
7. Harris, N.G. (1990) "A Simpler Southern?", *Modern Rlys.* 47 pp. 586-587, 600.
8. Heaps, C. (1990) "Docklands: the Growing Railway", *Modern Rlys.* 47 pp. 197-200.
9. Murray, I. (1989) "Keeping the Trains on Time", *InterCity* pp. 27-28.
10. Rodley, J.W.E. & Harris, N.G. (1988) "Why are Trains Late?", *Modern Rlys.* 45 pp. 634-636.

11. Weston, J.G. & Wheaton, V.A. (1991) "Train Service Model User Guide", Operational Research Note 91/1, London Underground.
12. Wilson, J. (1989) "Anglian Response", *Modern Rlys.* 46. p.492.
13. Wonnacott, T.H. & Wonnacott, R.J. (1981) "Regression: A Second Course in Statistics".

13. Personnel Planning

Tom Greaves

Introduction
When planning passenger railways, there are several key personnel issues. The objective of this paper is to highlight the problems likely to be encountered, concentrating on the train crew activity, which is probably the area presenting the major pitfalls.

Task Vulnerability
The most vulnerable area of the railway personnel function is that of the provision and direction of train crew and control staff, where staff are dispersed. Without responsible staff and effective management working to guidelines and control systems, the rail system will fail.

Technological development over recent years has considerably altered the direct responsibilities within the railway. In particular, technology has materially helped in the fields of signalling, radio, traction and rolling stock maintenance. This has been caused by higher degrees of automation, diagnostics, reliability and a better understanding of effective component lives.

Over the past 15 years the ratio of incidents deemed to be the responsibility of signal staff and drivers have altered from 1:1 to 1:4. The redistribution of hazard responsibility has occurred largely by technological innovation in signalbox and control system design. Today, the signalman in a power box almost has to engineer a mistake, whereas train driving is still essentially a manual task. However, it must be emphasised that all rail staff carry a high degree of responsibility and authority compared to most jobs within the same wage range.

Whilst managerial responsibilities and controls apply to all railway staff, drivers have a high degree of direct responsibility, and an analysis of the requirements for them is helpful:

1. Self discipline and the maintenance of personal standards are vital. The appreciation of task responsibility is essential, and there is a need for a high degree of personal reliability and dedication to the task.

143

2. The unsociable elements of the task are important when viewed against current perceptions of normal working practice. In particular, the need for adequate sleep and the abstinence from taking alcohol before the next turn of duty influence the social implications of the task. However, much is dependent upon the type of system and operation, the quest for economy being likely to demand shift (and possibly also irregular hour) working. The need to be on call for lengthy periods and being flexible in the interest of service also load the task profile.

The above qualities are those that must be present to undertake the normal scheduled day-to-day duties. Even fully automatic systems have to take account of unplanned events. Organized planned systems of recovery using both manual and automated activities can be inbuilt into the system. It is in this failure mode where the operators' initiative training is fundamental. It is in such circumstances where errors can easily be made, resulting not only in service disruption but also the prejudice of safety. With these thoughts in mind it is imperative to prepare detailed job descriptions, where either recruitment or job conversion is required.

Job Descriptions
The staff qualities detailed above must be reflected in the job description. Much depends upon the type of rail business the system undertakes. The most difficult applications are the multi-business rail systems, which have to incorporate outside influences, such as through traffic and feeder systems. The basic hours of employment, the shift system, the specific type of shift system, the proportion of free time, the number of days a week and (where applicable) the method of covering weekends should be highlighted when planning for new services. Tasks must be specified in detail with the specific responsibilities in relation to the organisational command chain.

Railway jobs generally fall into three categories: (a) commercial (e.g. selling tickets); (b) operational (e.g. signalling); and (c) technical and/or maintenance. Although there are reasons for a degree of dedication or role separation, staff flexibility has enabled significant advances in productivity. The development of much more cost-effective rail systems demands the overlapping of the traditional functional roles.

As a driver is probably to be provided in all but fully automatic train operated systems, then role combination must be an objective. As an example, the commercial role of the driver using train public address systems (especially in suburban train operation) not only improves

144

productivity and customer awareness but can combat boredom. The requirement to increase business awareness in what was previously a purely operative role is of considerable advantage as it is the passengers who pay the bills. To avoid confusion and wasted training later, these issues must be clear in the job description, as once training has started the expense to the company or business is considerable.

Finally, the remuneration and pension conditions should be made clear and financial participation in the business, such as share schemes or profit sharing should not be overlooked. Although railways rely on a degree of personal dedication and enthusiasm from the employee, it is the pay cheque that is the prime motivator.

Recruitment and Training

If new rail services involve increases in the number of train miles run, then attention will need to be given at an early stage to recruiting and training extra staff, as there can be a significant lead time in these activities. This may particularly be the case if railway development is occurring in an area of low unemployment as it may be necessary to recruit or transfer staff from elsewhere. The problem can be reduced if, for instance, guards (already with some knowledge of the system) are retrained to be drivers whilst new staff are simultaneously brought in as guards; this process also helps create sensible career progressions in an industry with a high age profile[1]. Where recruitment is difficult, it may impinge upon service introduction (e.g. the introduction of an all-day service on BR's South London Line was dependent upon the availability of one-person-operated (opo) rolling stock). It can also affect the service frequency v train length balance when determining how to provide a given level of capacity (see chapter 11), and could affect service viability altogether.

Lack of attention to recruitment detail in the past was partially excused by most railway posts being apprenticeship based. For a number of years a young person acted in a subordinate role with their performance constantly monitored and directed (e.g., a signalbox assistant under the watchful eye of the more experienced signalman). The irresponsible and the unreliable were therefore weeded out, or altered their ways and attitudes under direction. Attitude, personality, general intelligence and knowledge can now be determined with an acceptable degree of reliability (particularly when using commercial testing methods). The real difficulty is in determining personal stability and maturity.

Psychological testing of rail staff has been standard procedure on many Western European railways, and has recently been adopted on

British Rail (BR). Methods are varied, and there are specific tests designed to highlight differing qualities and degrees of competence. Successfully applied, this type of testing can provide a high degree of insurance in recruitment, initial and refresher training.

Most traditional recruitment methods are still worthy of consideration. These include recruiting staff from established transport families, where competence, reliability and stability have been proved in practice. Such family recruitment often provides a monitoring control that cannot be quantified in financial terms. References from previous employees, universities, schools and people commanding respect through position or experiences are of value and should be considered carefully.

Whether training is either for initial recruits or for existing staff transferring from other duties, modular block training systems have found favour. They have proved to be cost-effective, replacing traditional methods where much time was spent in supporting or observing the tasks to be undertaken. The diversity of systems means that the type and length of training periods must vary significantly. However, training staff who are to have a vital role in the railway cannot be cut short. The minimum periods of training range between three months (for a simple-network light rail system) to a year (for a multi-business heavy rail network with a variety of traction types).

It is usual practice on railways (for safety reasons) for drivers to be "passed" to drive only certain types of rolling stock or over certain routes. Conventional wisdom has it that only thus will drivers be able to respond to any problems that arise. This practice may, however, result in boredom or a loss of operational flexibility, e.g. in adverse weather.

If a new rail route is being planned, then sufficient time must be allowed for traincrew to undertake such route training (and for maintenance staff to get hands-on experience of any new rolling stock). To ensure a career progression, drivers' duties at a depot may be split into "links" comprising duties of differing complexity and pay. It may therefore be possible to minimise the training period for new services by only training one link of drivers. The first few trains of any batch built usually spend time being test-driven. During this period faults may be discovered. These faults can be rectified without the inconvenience and disastrous public relations that these would incur if they occurred in proper service (as happened with BR's APT train in 1984).

Simulator training is a developing practical alternative to some manual training. The initial cost of dynamic simulators can be as high as £3 million, and therefore this type of training has only rarely been

146

adopted. However, simulators of more limited capacity are being increasingly used e.g., for system training, reactions to emergencies, and braking techniques.

For rapid transit systems, simulators are now available at a cost of around £700,000 and can save a considerable amount of training time. They are particularly useful for updating and system revisions. In parallel, personal computer (p.c.) packages are available that can provide updating reviews and rules/regulations training. Advantages of such systems include random selection from the data bank, and tests or reviews that are seen to be fair. Similar training packages can be developed where the driver or operator can practice at will, when there is spare time available between duties.

Rostering and Scheduling

The objective of any rostering or scheduling exercise is to obtain the highest productivity from the workforce without impinging on legal requirements, service reliability, or the ability of staff to change between duties. It also must protect staff from fatigue, and ensure that the service can be run safely without introducing hazards caused by human failing or stress.

To meet the above, basic parameters have to be set when planning a new service. Typical conditions that might be applied are as follows:

(i)   scheduled rostering to be between 7 and 9 hours per duty;
(ii) allowances for physical needs break of up to 20 minutes between the third hour of duty and the fifth hour of duty;
(iii) a limitation in non-stop working of three hours subject to some slight variation where working is continuous but scheduled stops are provided.

The basis of rostering may be five days per week, providing one weekday free of duty and Sunday covered rotationally or by volunteers. The latter is undesirable as it leaves the railway dependent on something outside its control. By arranging Sunday as an additional day, staff earnings can be inflated, since Sunday staffing requirements are usually much less than on weekdays. On the other hand, full seven-day rostering is becoming a more attractive management proposition for suburban passenger light rail systems. Although such a system requires more staff on the books, this is balanced by system reliability and a reduction in overtime worked.

To meet necessary social requirements, it is of course attractive to group days off in blocks in order to equate to normal weekends. Such arrangements are perhaps best negotiated with the staff, as much depends upon the type of service and area of working. Computer rostering packages are now available and most rail systems have built up their own p.c. systems applying their specific conditions of service.

Holiday cover has to be carefully monitored, and it is normal to arrange a minimum of two weeks per driver during the peak of acceptable Summer leave (May-September). The balance is taken during the rest of the year. This may still lead to problems if there is a shortfall of staff since services may suffer around popular holiday periods.

Many studies have been undertaken in an attempt to understand what causes lack of attention in driving. The research has particularly looked at signals passed at danger (SPAD) and the adoption of malpractices. Boredom is one underlying factor, and may be relieved by more frequent breaks or changing between trains or lines. Some European railways, for instance, limit continual working more than twice over the same route, with the third round trip covering a different location. The suggested rostering guidelines must therefore be interpreted as indicative only. Specific studies should be undertaken of the type of service, the route and the conditions applied.

Cab design and environment also play an important part in determining the conditions of service and the applied rostering. Trains likely to induce boredom are likely to have sophisticated aids to driving, such as automatic train control or over-ride protection systems that avoid the driver making a serious mistake. Basic instrumentation is essential and diagnostic systems helping the driver in taking the right corrective action when incidents occur are necessary on all types of rolling stock. Energy monitoring and control systems are becoming increasingly attractive owing to the cost of energy being significant, when the whole life-cycle cost of traction design is considered (see chapter 15)? Although such aspects of cab design may be considered remote from the specific rostering activity, they however relate to the duty time and concentration levels required by the driver. Heating, noise and fresh air changes are also issues that cannot be viewed in isolation, and the personnel manager must be involved here too.

Performance Monitoring

All staff are susceptible to error, but as safety is paramount on a railway, then performance monitoring is essential. Casual meetings at signing-on points or the occasional unexpected attendance of inspectors in order to assess attitude or fitness for service are both costly and ineffective. It must be emphasised that performance monitoring is required not only for new recruits, but also for established experienced staff. Deterioration of health, sight and mind can occur, but without recognition until serious incident occurs. Also, drivers tend to be self-reliant and proud, and those of them with considerable experience and a clean record do not take kindly to regular monitoring techniques; also, drivers are often controlled by people without the same expertise. It is therefore imperative to have an inspector or manager with whom a driver can have respect for and identify. Many rail systems have a method of using junior managers within this role, but this is not always satisfactory.

Recent railway organisational changes have not always been reflected amongst managers. Attitudes in leadership and drive can be lacking, seriously affecting the total performance of the system. The major problem as seen from the ground force is managers' lack of professionalism in the workers' own specific profession. This has been brought about by managers taking a much wider role. Training and development in the specific profession can enable the manager to have greater confidence and surety in actions, whilst clarifying the command structure is critical (see chapter 2).

When error occurs, however, responsibility should go beyond the driver or operator directly concerned; there is an equal managerial failing. A careful examination of the driver: inspector relationship, and of standards and performance levels must be made. This can be satisfactorily achieved by the specific allocation of drivers to inspectors, by which the latter is aware of the drivers' strengths and weaknesses, and can concentrate on particular problems. This group system of management with one inspector (Chef de Traction Principal on SNCF) between 25 and 35 train crew has worked exceedingly effectively in France and the Benelux countries, and is being introduced in some parts of BR.

Monitoring should not only be concentrated upon the ability to drive precisely and keep time, but also on the social aspects such as tendencies towards alcoholism, indiscipline and even drugs. Importantly, when mistakes are made, it is frequently not through professional incompetence but often worrying personal factors, which cause drivers' minds to wander or be distracted (e.g. family problems, ill health, or infidelity). These can only be detected by having a personal and trustworthy relationship with a monitoring or supervisory element within the industry. There are some who would perceive this as an incursion into personal liberties, but to the railway manager operational safety must override all issues. For this reason inspector training, review sessions and counselling services are an important part of the management personnel system. The general objective is the ability to detect potential danger before it strikes.

Technology also has its part to play in incident avoidance, and for example on-train recorders are now being introduced on several railways (including, at last, BR and LUL) now that electronic developments enable recorders to be provided at a low cost[2]. These recorders enable the monitoring of driver performance and reaction time, besides technical performance monitoring. Electronic processing enables speedy and cost effective assessments to be made. This can be either by random selection or by extraction according to inspectors' wishes, where it is known that there are potential problems or hazard areas. Tact and care are again required. There is an equal need for training and guidance of managers in these techniques as there are in driving, signalling and other rail staff in the performance of their duties.

Union and Industrial Representation
Irrespective of the politics of the day, any large labour group occupying a position that can affect the service and performance of the railway will have some degree of representation by a labour group. This may be a full trade union organisation or local group spokesperson. The trade unions over recent years have also undergone considerable changes in both attitude and influence.

For successful rail operation, there is a need to update staff and unions constantly, keeping them fully in the picture about developments, objectives and performance. For example, trade unions are not as adverse to change as is commonly believed. If change is to be effected, it is imperative for management to prove the necessity for change. It is essential to lead with confidence and conviction, and to prove that management action is correct and just.

Providing these conditions are met, continued opposition is unlikely. Where there have been failings and industrial action, responsibility has been a shared one and usually associated with a total lack of effective communication. Many trade union objections raised about railway developments are associated with raising the reward or payment for their members.

An example of trade union cooperation in a difficult area was the introduction of data recorders. The trade union view was that they did not support malpractice or unprofessional working. Providing the monitoring was open, they had few reservations and, indeed, supported the provision of data recorders. For many years they had reservations concerning the number of incidents of SPAD resulting in staff discipline, but they believed that, on occasions, the equipment (rather than the driver) was at fault.

Discipline

Even with the finest labour force, a superb organisation and effective management, errors, malpractice and indiscipline will occur from time to time. A disciplinary code has to be developed and updated as necessary. With key operational roles, it is imperative that when discipline is applied, a minimum of distraction to job operation is assured. So, for serious errors involving safety, or with hazard implications pending full investigation, precautionary suspension is a sensible practice to adopt. Investigations need to be speedy and fair, to minimise distraction. For that reason, workers should be charged with a written offence and not more than three days should elapse before the discipline decision is made.

Where serious incident and accidents have occurred, careful consideration must be given to determination of responsbility and discipline subsequently applied. Traditional railway practice has been that, for example, a driver is charged with SPAD, but not with the results of the resulting incident or disaster. The effect of the error has generally been perceived to be an industrial responsibility. There is a good reason for this, in that a driver drives to a code of practice that includes mandatory controlling of their trains, and stopping at a signal set at danger irrespective of the conditions. The determination of the working practices and controls have always been one within the railway and the management should therefore share in any responsibility for the failings of their staff. Regrettably, there is an increasing demand by the public at large for retribution. It should be noted that the tendency to move towards common law is a double-edged sword, since railway pay has for many years been somewhat low. If responsibility is transferred from the industry to the individual, then one could legitimately expect high financial payment for specific turns of duty. Incidents emphasise the importance of effective rostering, conditions of service, management controls, self discipline and leadership, resulting in a cost-effective safe and secure railway business.

References

1. Ford, R. (1985) "Shaping BR's Traction and Traincrew Policy for the 1990s", Modern Rlys. 42 pp354-356, 367.
2. Vaughan, G. (1991) "The Black Box Flight Recorder has been found", Rail 153, July 24 - August 6.

14. Civil Engineering: Finding an Alignment

David Catling

Introduction

This chapter describes the civil engineer's role in the inter-disciplinary and iterative process by which an identified corridor of public transport demand is slowly developed into a safe, feasible, direct, environmentally-acceptable, economical and cost-effective railway alignment.

It lists the basic factors and principles to be taken into account, then illustrates their application by two different practical examples: the proposed London Crossrail (where a clearly defined traffic demand exists), and London's Docklands Light Railway, where the railway's role was to *generate* the demand.

The Civil Engineer's Key Role

The civil engineer has a key role at all stages of the planning and building of a new railway for a number of reasons. Even in a small scheme, civil engineering costs will predominate in the total capital budget. A project's whole financial viability and the granting of funding to build a new railway will therefore almost certainly depend on keeping civil engineering costs to an acceptable level, but without prejudicing safety, the life of structures, or the environment. To achieve this, the civil engineer must be involved right from the very beginning.

At the preliminary evaluation stage when various possible options are being considered (see chapter 4), the civil engineer can provide notional unit costs to synthesise total system costs sufficiently accurately for cost/benefit assessment of the various options. He can advise whether certain theoretically attractive options would be totally impracticable and/or prohibitively expensive, e.g. involving costly tunnelling in rocky, bad or wet ground, avoiding existing and proposed major subterranean obstacles, crossing over or under waterways, and suggest suitable alternatives.

The Evolutionary and Iterative Process

In order to develop a rail system with minimum total capital and operating life cycle costs, it is essential to recognise the interdependence of all the principal technical civil, mechanical, and electrical engineering parameters (see Fig. 14.1), and to evolve the optimum solution by an iterative process. For example, in deciding on the optimum train performance, train length, capacity and service frequency to meet a given predicted demand for a new suburban rail system with a significant amount of tunnelling, a number of directly inter-related variables must be considered. To meet a given peak demand cost-effectively with the minimum numbers of trains and crews to run the service, the trains should ideally be run at the widest acceptable interval without affecting passenger demand, and have (a) individual coaches as long and as wide as possible; (b) the maximum acceptable number of coaches per train; and (c) the highest possible scheduled speed.

However, the practical application of these principles will have the following interactive effects on the principal technical parameters, which readers may wish to trace for themselves from Figure 14.1. *Vehicle length, width, height, and bogie centres* between them affect the width of the alignment, the size and cost of any elevated structures or tunnels, and the minimum horizontal and vertical curvatures; these can in turn constrain the choice and cost of the alignment. *Maximum train length* determines the lengths and costs of station platforms and sidings (which can be significant in tunnel), the loading on bridges and viaducts, and the size and layout of depot(s); it also influences the signalling.

High schedule speeds require a high performance train with high acceleration and braking rates, to reduce inter-station run times. This requires more traction equipment and motors, which in turn increase both the total train weight and the individual sprung and unsprung wheel weights in rail. These loadings then determine the size and cost of any elevated structures, and also affect the complex interactions between vehicle suspension and rail support, which influence the level of noise and vibration (see chapter 19).

High performance, heavier trains also increase total electrical energy consumption and peak current demands, which can increase the number and size of substations (unless high voltage AC power supply is used); these must be fairly evenly spaced along the route, on sites with good unrestricted road access and convenient adequate high voltage electricity supplies, but such sites may be difficult to find. *High power demands* also affect the power supply between the substation and the train; the trackside power supply may require larger wire cross-sections to limit the voltage drop, and to ensure protection against electrical faults. If overhead, heavier wires may require mast spacing.

PERMANENT WAY	DEMAND	STATIONS
Type of Base	Routes	Platform Length
Track Formation	Service Patterns	Platform Width
Rail Weight/Fastening	Stations and	Entrances/Exits
Noise/Vibration Reduction	Interchanges	(number, location, width)
Current Leakage Precautions	Lines and Connections	
	Peak Frequencies	
	Journey Times	
	Peak Flows	

ALIGNMENTS	Peak Boardings/ Alightings	DEPOTS/SIDINGS
At-Grade/Elevated/ Below Ground		Location(s)
Width		Sizes
Height		Facilities
Horizontal Curvature	ROLLING STOCK	
Vertical Curvature	Vehicle Dimensions	
Max. Grade (short/ sustained)	Swept Volume	
	Max. Train Length	
	Passenger Capacity	
STRUCTURES	Acceleration Rate	POWER SUPPLY
Elevated (Viaduct/ Embankment/Bridge)	Doors (no. & size)	Track Voltage
	Braking Rate	Substations
Cutting	Maximum Speed	(number, locations)
Tunnel (Cut-and-Cover/ Bored)	Total Train Weight	H T Supply
	Max. Axle Loading	Overhead Wires
	Min. Wheel Diameter	(section, supports)
	No. of Trains	Low-Level (section, type)
		Leakage Detection

Readers are invited to trace through for themselves the linkages between the elements, and the reasons for the interdependencies.

Fig. 14.1   Interaction and Interdependence of Principal Parameters.

Should be specified for initial and final networks, especially for constraints affecting the whole system e.g. curvatures, gradients, route segregation

Low level current collection may need heavier or special conductor rails.

Scheduled speed can also be increased by reducing the total station dwell times in a round trip. These are a function of (a) *individual station stop times*, determined for each particular station by the total boarding and alighting movements, the number, spacing and width of the train doors and the vehicle interior layout, the station layout, platform widths, entrances, exits and interchange passages (see chapter 5); and (b) *the total number of stations* in an end-to-end journey (The trade-off between inter-station spacing and passenger demand is considered in Chapter 4, and can also have a major effect on total cost, especially for underground railways.)

Service frequencies determine the total number of annual movements over elevated and other structures and influence their fatigue life. Peak frequencies also affect the numbers of trains and the power supply.

Initial Steps in Developing a Railway Alignment[7,8,9]

Before starting the detailed planning of an alignment for a new railway to run through an existing developed city, a number of initial decisions should have been made. First, there should be agreement on the type of railway, vehicle size and maximum train length, after an objective joint analysis with the civil engineer of all feasible options (see the discussion of levels of segregation in chapter 4). Secondly, the preferred route and station location, and any required interchanges with existing railways, shoud have been broadly specified. Thirdly, the alignment should be as direct and as near to the surface as possible if below ground. Fourthly, the alignment should take account of the Environmental Assessment Study (see chapter 18) which is now required for a new railway under European Community legislation, and of any other potentially-contentious issues likely to affect the passage through Parliament of the necessary legislation (see chapter 8).

Initially, much necessary preliminary information needs to be collected, and preferred initial standards developed, accepting that those relating to gradients and curves may have to be modified later, in the light of practical and/or economic constraints. All existing Ordnance Survey or other officially published ground plans in the alignment corridor will need to be acquired, commissioning any necessary aerial and other surveys. Information on existing sub-surface obstructions of Statutory Authorities' sewers, water mains, cables, other underground services, deep pile foundations, historic or other buildings will also be needed, as these may affect the line and level of a tunnel, station siting and access, or the foundations of an elevated alignment.

(Note that the railway as the newcomer has to bear the often considerable cost of any necessary diversions or special protective measures to existing services, or to avoid them altogether if their diversion is impracticable).

All other factors which could possibly affect alignment and level need to be assessed, such as ground conditions at different strata, water levels, extreme local climatic or other conditions (e.g. tropical temperatures and rainstorms (Singapore), typhoons (Hong Kong), earthquakes (San Francisco)) which could possibly affect alignment and type of construction, or require special measures such as flood protection and tunnel cooling. Additional ground and borehole surveys need to be commissioned as necessary, and any areas or strata where work would be prohibitively expensive or impracticable identified. The details and timetable of any planned major developments along the proposed route (where the railway and the development might be constructed together, with potential major savings in cost and time) also need to be established.

The next step on an entirely new railway is for the Civil and Rolling Stock Engineers jointly to develop the optimum rolling stock dimensions and alignment cross-sections in a complex iterative process (ref. 10 pp. 330-373).

The *Track Gauge* is assumed fixed at the standard rail spacing of 1435mm (4ft 8.5in), used by most European railways. However, the *Static Loading Gauge*, which is the maximum permitted cross-section of a stationary vehicle on straight and level track, can vary enormously. Britain has a smaller loading gauge than the Continent, and London's tube railways are even smaller. (A still smaller Glasgow Subway car would almost fit *inside* a Hong Kong Mass Transit car). Larger loading gauges permit greater train capacity, and even the use of double-deck stock (see Fig. 22.2), but of course require more spacious alignments and larger tunnels.

The *Developed Kinematic Envelope* (DKE) is then calculated, based on an assumed vehicle size and type. The DKE is the line around the track in a plane normal to the vehicle which encloses its extreme position under all conditions of speed and load on straight and level track, including dynamic body movements, wear and tolerances on suspension, wheels and track. It also has to take account of all the possible effects of curvature, track superelevation, preferred horizontal and vertical limiting curvatures, given speeds at particular locations, vehicle end and centre throw (determined by the proposed body length, width, and bogie centres).

Finally the *Swept Path* is derived, which is the DKE enlarged to take account of the required minimum clearances to fixed structures, adjoining tracks, or walkways. The width of a double track alignment and diameter or cross-section of any single bore or twin track tunnels can then be set out, allowing for the form of track construction, overhead or low-level current collection, and possibly a side walkway for emergency de-training.

The power/weight ratio of the proposed trains should be checked for adequacy under specified fault conditions e.g. for "pushing out" a fully loaded defective train with parking brakes applied on the steepest ruling gradient. Other curve and gradient standards should be confirmed (e.g. station platforms, sidings and depot tracks should wherever possible be straight and level; in tunnels a minimum gradient of 0.25% between stations assists drainage). A sub-surface railway may be able to apply a "hump station" profile with falling and rising gradients leaving and approaching stations to assist acceleration and braking respectively. This was first introduced on London's Central Line Tube, and then 60 years later on the Victoria Line (ref 9, p30).

System	Tunnel Diameter	Max. Speed	Max. Grade	Min. Curve Radius Horiz.	Vertical	Max. Cant
	m	km/h	%	m	m	mm
London (tube)	3.8	80[A]	2.0	400(200)	1600	152
Stockholm[B]						
Line 1		80	4.0	200	1500	G
Line 2		80	4.0	250	2000	G
Line 3		90	4.0	600	4000	G
Singapore	5.2	80	2.5 (3.3)	400 (200)	1600	150
London Crossrail	6.0	100[C]	2.5 (3.3)	500 (300)	1600[C]	150
London Docklands	5.0	80	3.0 (6.0)	300[D]	4000[E]	100[F]

Preferred values shown first (maxima necessary to achieve required alignment in brackets).

Notes:
A: In tunnel.
B: Note progressive development in standards. Tunnel diameters not quoted as bored tunnels not used.
C: Max. speed of 160km/h and vertical radius of 3000m used for outer, surface sections.
D: For ballasted track; for non-ballasted track a radius of only 40m was permitted.
E: For unrestricted speed; a vertical radius of only 1000m was permitted for sections with restricted maximum speed.
F: Target figure; an absolute maximum of 150mm cant was used.
G: Not available.

Table 14.1   Civil Engineering Data for New Running Lines.

157

In general, of course, a new railway will try to specify the most generous curves and easiest gradients without prejudicing flexibility of choice of route or overall cost in order to maximise train performance; typical examples are shown in Table 14.1. There are also standards for the transitions into curves and the rate of application of curvature and superelevation, to improve passenger comfort and reduce rail and wheel wear[6].

These standard are in sharp contrast to the early London tube railways, where the policy was for lines to follow under roads in order to reduce the cost of purchasing easements under private property (ref.9, p29). Moreover, gradual transitions between straight track and horizontal single curves, or between adjoining reverse curves of opposite hand, or into vertical curves, were considered unnecessary. The practical consequences are, for example, that trains for London's Central Line will always have to be designed to fit the original 1897 tunnels of only 3.56m diameter, with particularly tight clearances around the positive rail, and a 60m line minimum operating radius, exacerbated by severe reverse and vertical curves without transitions. These all impose severe and costly constraints on the physical design of the trains (e.g. for the essential minimum electrical clearances around the bogie-mounted shoegear, and to avoid the fracturing of the inter-car drawbars which occurred on pre-War tube trains due to the sharp and sudden vertical curves).

Given the principal dimensions, types of ground strata, topography and climate, initial choices can be made about the following likely forms of construction and levels on various parts of the route[7,8]. *Ground level* *("at grade")* gives low cost alignments and stations with good access but there is probably little scope for this on a new route in a developed city, except for a manually driven light railway; the "barrier" or severance effects of the new alignment could be unacceptable (see chapter18). An *open shallow cutting* reduces visual and audible intrusion in environmentally sensitive areas without undue severance, but has limited possible application in a developed city, and could incur costly service diversions. *Elevated or viaduct* reinforced concrete structures can provide full road height clearances without severance but are more costly, visually and audibly intrusive than at grade and incur increased station costs. *Embankments* can be less expensive but have the barrier effect. *Shallow cut and cover tunnels* reduce visual and audible intrusion and have no permanent land take and only moderate station costs, but can incur major disruption during construction and service diversions if under streets; protective measures for existing buildings are required, and therefore these are of limited application in built up cities with deep pile foundations and other major obstructions. *Deep bored tunnels* give the greatest choice of alignment and flexibility to avoid costly obstructions without permanent land take and have potential for hump stations, but at greatly increased construction and station cost, liability to tunnel settlement, increased passenger access time, and a high cost of additional precautions (e.g. for fire, evacuation and ventilation); moreover, they are only feasible in suitable ground.

The London Crossrail[5]

This proposed line across London, modelled on the trans-Paris RER, was recommended in the 1989 Central London Rail Study[4], and received Government approval in principle in the same year. The following details illustrate the complexities, challenges and inevitable compromises facing the civil engineer when applying the general considerations listed earlier to find a feasible alignment for such a huge project through a great historic city, where new developments with deep pile foundations are proceeding apace. Nearly 9 km of the Central section has to be in tunnel, extending between West of Paddington and East of Liverpool Street stations (Fig 14.2), with five underground stations providing interchange with Underground and BR lines. The

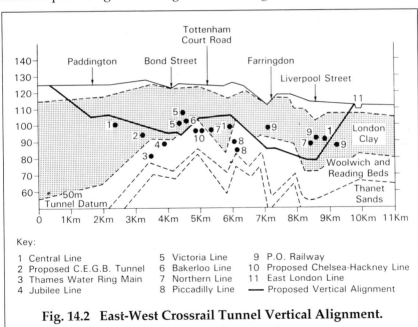

Fig. 14.2 East-West Crossrail Tunnel Vertical Alignment.

159

number of stations is a compromise between cost and interchange maximisation against an acceptable journey time. Two possible alignments were rejected because they would be too deep (and below the good tunnelling London Clay strata), have too tight reverse curves, or would not provide all the required interchanges.

The preferred option varies in depth between 20 and 40m, and is mostly in the London Clay, but will still have alignment constraints (principally to avoid conflict with other tunnels and piled foundations), curvatures down to 300m (but only near stations where speeds are low), several 1000m radius platforms, and widely separated tracks at Holborn. It was difficult to avoid unacceptable gradients, or to locate the stations on humps, as the alignment has to cross over and under existing tube lines five or four times respectively, and other existing obstacles (see Fig. 14.2). The maximum sustained gradient is limited to 2.5%, with a maximum of 3.3% at the east end of the tunnel. There are 300 current planning applications adjacent to the route, but the proposed alignment has now been safeguarded by directives issued by the Department of Transport under the Town and Country Planning Act, pending Royal Assent of the Parliamentary Bill to be deposited in November 1991.

The tunnelling will be a formidable task, with running tunnels 6m in diameter, for full-size British Rail and LUL trains with overhead electrification, and a side walkway for emergency detraining; station tunnels are 8-9m diameter, with 4m width platforms initially 190m long for 8 car trains, but with provision for extending to 280m for 12 car trains. However, the cost of providing full intermediate reversing facilities and a 13m diameter, 130m long tunnel for an emergency crossover proved prohibitive.

For environmental reasons the running tunnels will be (unusually) driven only from the two ends, with the spoil removed and tunnel segments delivered by rail, rather than by road. Draught relief and ventilation shafts up to 13m diameter will be provided at and between stations, the latter also serving for emergency escape. The station works will be very costly and protracted, with only limited working sites at some stations. The stations must have convenient interchange and safe means of access and evacuation to the latest requirements, with dual ticket halls, escalators and lifts for the disabled. Given a reasonable passage of the Bill through Parliament and the availability of funds, however, the Line could be open before the year 2000.

The Docklands Light Railway (DLR)[2, 3, 11]

The previous sections have tried to show that the planning of a new

160

railway to meet a well-defined traffic demand in a highly developed city can proceed in an orderly and logical sequence, albeit a highly complex and lengthy process, with many factors, options and difficult decisions.

However, in the case of Docklands, the situation was completely reversed. The railway was seen as the catalyst to attract international developers to the largest city site in Europe, to be developed around the derelict former London Docks. This once thriving area had declined to become a depressed and deprived inner city wasteland[11] but, when the DLR was being planned in the early 1980s, there was virtually no new development, and the area was poorly served by public transport. The traffic demand forecasts were therefore sketchy, and the predicted traffic levels of only 2-3000 passengers in the peak hour were more appropriate to an enhanced bus service than to a new fixed track system, and would not justify a new railway on transport planning grounds alone. The uncertain location and scale of any development, and the future role of the remaining Docks and dockside building, made even the clear choice of route uncertain.

A suggest limited budget of around £50M ruled out earlier proposals for an extension of the London Underground, and pointed to the maximum use of the extensive existing surface railway rights of way around the Docks, linked into a network by a system capable of negotiating sharp curves and steep gradients at modest cost, with the possibility of street running. Thus light rail was virtually the only possible choice on grounds of construction cost, suitability for the predicted traffic levels and flexibility of choice of alignment and level.

The numerous initial route options were reduced to two, an East-West link to the City, and a complementary North-South link to the residential areas of North-East London, joining in an elevated triangular junction to form a spine down the centre of the Isle of Dogs. However, uncertainties remained in a number of areas, including the crossing of the Docks themselves, the future navigational requirements of which were undecided. In 1982 the Government approved the construction of these two initial lines for a strictly limited cash out-turn of £77M, to open within five years for maximum benefit to the new developments. These two principal requirements, coupled with a desire to use the latest proven technology, led to a number of changes. The North-South link involved extensive street running along a main road into London, and fears of obtaining the necessary Parliamentary powers, and of road congestion affecting rail reliability, led to a change to a segregated route along a surplus BR single track to Stratford (see Figure 14.3), subject to no extra cost. Once this had been agreed, very little of the total initial 12 route-km remained at ground level. In order to keep open the option of a wholly segregated system, with the possibility of partial or complete automation, provision was (unusually) made in the London Docklands Railway No. 1 Parliamentary Bill for the vertical height of the critical 0.5km section to be either at ground level or elevated.

Progress was difficult. About three-quarters of the route ran on ex-BR tracks or alignments, which needed to be cleared, rebuilt or refurbished, whilst maintaining full safety over adjoining BR operational tracks and protecting the rights of some 200 tenants of the railway arches where it was on viaduct. The number of stations, quality and appearance of new structures (including a long single span across a planned new road), type of system and number of trains all had to be balanced within the budget. London Transport placed a single "design and construct" contract for the whole railway, to ensure completion on time and within budget. Despite the extensive use of existing railway rights of way, and the relatively sophisticated automated system finally chosen, some two-thirds of the total contract price was for civil and building related works.

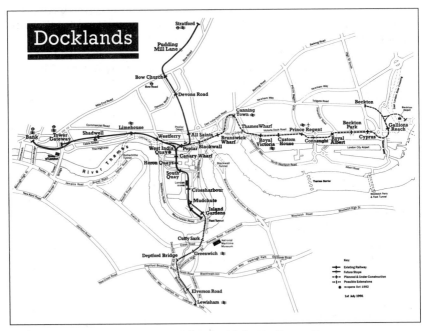

Fig. 14.3 The Docklands Light Railway System.

The whole basis of the traffic demands and patterns then changed dramatically, with a proposed new development on Canary Wharf of some 10M sq.ft. of offices and 50,000 employees, leading to a tenfold increase in the traffic demand, and an upgrading of the new structures, signalling and power supply to cater for higher-frequency double-length trains.

Even before it even opened, extensions were being planned; developers contributed extensively to a 1.8km Western link to Bank (see chapter 20). Very difficult tunnelling in sensitive areas under the City of London leads to platforms 42m below ground and with interchange with three other underground lines. Work has begun on an 8km extension to Beckton, with 13 additional stations, and plans are well advanced for a 3.8km Southern extension under the River Thames to Greenwich and Lewisham (see Figure 14.3).

Thus the type, route and character of the railway have change dramatically, far beyond the wildest dreams of the original railway planners, who were trying hard to justify a simple low cost railway in preference to an improved bus service.

Conclusions

This chapter has sought to set out the extremely complex and lengthy process by which a traffic route is developed into a safe, feasible, appropriate and viable railway alignment. This requires a combination of unwavering broad vision of the ultimate goal, but with a flexible response to the constant new factors which emerge as the project progresses, many of which will be outside the civil engineer's control. In parallel with these broad requirements must go the continuous fullest detailed study of all the factors listed. Only thus can success be ensured for a project of such magnitude, which will have such a major and permanent effect on a city's infrastructure. The alternative is unthinkable.

Further Reading and Acknowledgements

The author gratefully acknowledges the extent to which he has quoted from the published works of his former London Transport colleagues. The references will provide valuable further reading; in particular, Vuchic's monumental work[10] is essential for any serious transport student.

References

1. Anon (1990) "£1.4Bn East-West Crossrail Promised", *Railway Gaz. Intnl.* p.826.

2. Bayman, R.E. & Jolly, S. (1988) "Docklands Light Railway Official handbook", Capital Transport Publishing and DLR Ltd.
3. Catling, D.T. (1985) "The Planning and Building of the Docklands Light Railway", Univ. of Leeds 17th Annual Seminar on Public Tranport Operations Research, Paper I.
4. Department of Transport et al. (1989) "Central London Rail Study".
5. Fergusson, J.C. (1990) "East-West Crossrail - Central London Tunnel Section", British Railways Board Civil Engng. Dept. Works Conference, Paper B.
6. Follenfant, H.G. (1968) "Underground Railway Construction", London transport.
7. Mead, D.R. (1990) "Civil Engineering Aspects of Route Planning", in Edwards, J.T. "Civil Engineering for Underground Rail Transport", Butterworths.
8. Skelton, E. (1987) "Route Planning", Inst of Civil Engineers Conference on Urban Railways and the Civil Engineer, paper 2 p27.
9. Turner, F.S.P. (1959) "Preliminary Planning for a New Tube Railway Across London" (the Victoria Line), *Proc. Inst. Civil Eng.* 12 pp19-38.
10. Vuchic, V.R. (1981) "Urban Public Transportation Systems and Technology", Prentice-Hall.
11. Willis, J.G. (1987) "Docklands - Planning the Initial Railway", *Jnl. of the Inst. of Highways & Transpn.* pp. 7-18 (Aug-Sept).

15. Traction and Rolling Stock

Roger Ford

Introduction

For the railway engineering team, optimising the use of the infrastructure is the dominant task. How this optimum is defined will vary, but generally it is based on a combination of journey time and capacity determined by planning and commercial considerations.

These two factors also influence the financial performance of the service as they determine its attractiveness and the ability to create revenue from the resulting demand. They are largely determined by the interaction between the performance of the trains and the control and signalling system. This applies equally to such disparate systems as the fully automated Docklands Light Railway in London and the TGV Nord high speed line linking Paris with the Channel Tunnel.

This chapter provides an outline of current practice in the technologies of traction and rolling stock and shows how they interdepend with signalling systems, already discussed in chapter 11.

Braking

We have already seen how 'your power to stop is your right to speed'. Two real life examples can illustrate the relationship between speed, braking power and signalling.

In the late 1960s, British Rail was faced with increasing competition from air and road on its InterCity routes. To reduce journey times maximum speed had to be increased from 160 km/h to 200 km/h. At the same time, the higher speed had to be achieved without extending existing multiple aspect signal spacing. The key to this problem was the development of the disc brake, plus electronic anti-wheel slide devices which allowed the braking rate to be increased from 7% of the force of gravity (g) to 9%g. As a result, InterCity 125 could stop from 200 km/h in the distance required by a conventionally braked train from 160 km/h. Braking made InterCity 125 possible.

Twenty years later French Railways was planning TGV Nord from Paris to the Channel Tunnel, Belgium and, ultimately, Germany. On the first Ligne a Grande Vitesse from Paris to Lyon the signalling system could achieve 5-minute headways with trains running at 270km/h and 2,100m block lengths. On TGV Atlantique to the West Coast, this was improved to 4-minute headways at 300km/h and a 2,000km block length. Both these systems used coded track circuits to display speeds in the cab.

TGV Nord was clearly going to be heavily utilised and increased capacity was required. To meet this demand a new signalling system was specified to give a 3min headway at 300km/h, but with a block length of only 1,500 metres. This is achieved by transmitting additional data from the trackside, compared with the system used on the other TGV lines. One result is that the drivers on TGV Nord are able to 'see' a further signalling block ahead through the addition of a flashing signal on the cab display.

Moving Block

On mass transit systems, in contrast, low speeds mean that braking distances are short. Trains need to run closely together for maximum capacity. With the block-based signalling systems described so far, the minimum practical headway is 1.5 - 2 mins. Modern computer technology allows the fixed block to be replaced by what is called moving block. In a typical moving block system, a central computer communicates with all the trains on the network, each of which has its own on board microprocessor. The central computer knows where all the trains are, how fast they are moving and in which direction.

This information is constantly updated and transmitted to the trains, which are also measuring how far they have travelled since the last update. Each train is thus able to calculate its safe speed, based on the distance to the train in front and the speed at which it is running.

Several mass transit operators have introduced moving block systems, the best known being the SACEM system of the RER in Paris. In most cases, operators exploit moving block, not to run to the absolute minimum headway possible, but to run more reliably at 1 - 2 min headways.

Traction Performance

There is a further factor in the capacity equation of concern to the planner. The acceleration of the train determines how fast it clears sections and how quickly it attains line speed after station stops or speed restrictions.

Acceleration is a function of installed power, the available adhesion and the number of axles powered. For intercity railways, acceleration is a lesser consideration. However, suburban and urban passenger systems require the highest acceleration rate commensurate with passenger comfort, which is around 1 m/s^2.

For maximum acceleration, all axles would be powered, but this is an expensive option. A typical British Rail suburban train like the Hunslet Class 323 for the West Midlands, West Yorkshire and North West England has two thirds of the axles powered. This gives an acceleration rate of 0.64m/s^2 fully laden, which is typical of modern vehicles.

Automatic Train Operation
Traction and signalling are completely integrated on modern mass transit railways where automatic train operation is employed. This goes far beyond the relatively simple task of driving the trains. Computer control offers a suite of operating strategies based on a constantly up-dated comparison between the actual service and the timetable in the database.

For example, to minimise energy consumption off-peak, trains can be instructed, via coded track circuits or trackside beacons, to maximise coasting while running to time. Alternatively, to recover from a delay, maximum performance can be implemented.

An important corollary of this system is that the train power control must also be computer based. Traditional train control based on notches or steps can prove to be incompatible with the infinitely-variable instructions from the computer, which can fall between notches.

Traction
Electric traction is the first choice of passenger railways. Advantages include: higher installed power, lower maintenance, greater reliability, unlimited range without refuelling, less local environmental pollution, ability to use a wide range of energy sources and greater energy efficiency.

State of the art electric traction equipment incorporates three phase electric motors and all-electronic power controls. These further reduce maintenance requirements and increase reliability. Other benefits of three phase drive include smaller, lighter motors for a given rating and simple regenerative braking. In regenerative braking, the motors are switched to run as generators to slow the train.

Regenerative Braking
Electricity produced in regeneration can be used by other trains or returned to the power supply on ac electrified lines. Energy savings of between 25-30% are achieved in practice. Substantial reduction in brake wear (a major maintenance expense on suburban trains) also results.

167

A further benefit, particularly when upgrading railways for higher capacity, is that regeneration reduces the overall energy consumption. Thus a more intensive service can be run without the costly upgrading of power supplies which would previously have been required. This was the basis of investment in the Networker train programme on British Rail's Network SouthEast

Costs

Analysis in mid 1991 of comparatively-rated European high speed locomotives showed that three phase drive imposed a cost premium of 40% over direct current drive. In the case of electric multiple units, where the benefits are considerably greater, the premium is approximately 20%. These differentials can be expected to diminish as the cost of power and control electronics continues its historic fall in real terms.

Power

With locomotives and power cars for high speed trains, installed power within an all up weight determined by axle load and wheel configuration is the key factor. For a typical European Bo-Bo (four axle) 250 km/h locomotive/power car with a 20 tonne axle load the continuous rating will be around 5 MW. Short term ratings of 6 MW are available.

A single power unit of this rating can haul an eight to ten coach train at up to 250 km/h. European railways tend to favour longer formations for high speed trains, requiring two power cars. For example, the German IC-Express has two 4.8 MW power cars capable of hauling 14 trailer cars, but initially formed with 12 cars to reduce capital cost.

A 20 tonne axle load is considered acceptable for high speed in Britain and Germany. French Railways specifies a 17 tonne axle load for its Lignes a Grande Vitesse.This clearly limits the installed power and for the first TGV, two axles on the coach adjacent to each four axle power car had to be motored as well. Later TGV used three-phase drive to pack sufficient power into the two four axle power cars.

However, despite using a further development of three-phase drive from Britain, the TGV-derived Trans-Manche Super Trains for service between Paris/Brussels and London have had to revert to motoring the two axles on the adjacent coaches. This is to allow for the weight of additional electrical equipment in the power car for operation on three voltages plus the train formation of 18 coaches.

168

High Speed Multiple Units

An alternative approach to high speed is the multiple unit with underfloor mounted electrical equipment rather than separate power cars. Two examples are the Japanese Shinkansen or 'Bullet trains' and the Italian ETR 450 'Pendolino'.

Initially, the Shinkansen had all vehicles powered. The current Series 100 has eight of its 12 cars powered for a combined rating of 11MW. Each traction motor is rated at 230 kW, compared with over 1,000 kW each for the four motors of a European high speed power car.

In Pendolino, 10 out of 11 cars are powered, each powered car having two 315 kW motors on one bogie. With what is effectively a high power Electric Multiple Unit with two thirds axles motored, acceleration rates equivalent to suburban trains can be achieved - 0.8 m/sec^2 in the case of ETR450 which compared with 0.78 m/sec^2 for an inner suburban Networker.

Diesel Traction

As the British Rail InterCity 125 shows (see Fig. 15.1), it is possible to run a high speed train service with diesel traction. This train is comparable with the French TGV, as is reflected in the 17 tonne axle load of the power car. To provide the 3.35MW needed for 200 km/h operation with seven coaches, twin power cars with high speed engines had to be used. Subsequently it was found that better-than-forecast aerodynamics allowed an additional coach to be added with no loss of performance.

Thus diesel power can provide an effective high speed service[1]. Nor is commercial success dependent on maximum speed operation. For example, a licence-built InterCity 125 in New South Wales, Australia is geared for a 160 km/h maximum speed to suit local track conditions. Despite this, the enhanced acceleration and braking rates plus an improved top speed over existing stock enabled journeys previously taking a day to become day returns.

With the spread of electrification and the introduction of high quality diesel multiple units, diesel locomotive haulage continues to diminish. Maximum ratings are in the 3MW region and lower powers are often adequate. Technical trends on modern diesel traction are towards greater fuel efficiency in engines and the adoption of three phase electric transmission.

Diesel Multiple Units (DMUs)

Of more interest to transport planners is the new generation of diesel multiple units now available. These offer the opportunity of substantial upgrading of non electrified routes, the aim being to match the passenger ambience of locomotive hauled intercity stock.

Fig. 15.1   Inter City 125 accelerates away from London Kings Cross.

In Germany, for example, a fleet of VT 610 two car tilting diesel electric multiple units, with a maximum tilt angle of 8°, was ordered for services between Nurnberg, Beyreuth and Hof. Two 485 kW engines give a 160 km/h top speed. Typical journey time improvements are Nurnberg-Beyreuth (92 km) in 56 min with two stops, compared with the previous 67 min with four stops, and Nurnberg-Hof (166 km) in 86 minwith four stops (previously 117 min with five stops).

In Denmark, the IC3 three-car DMU has four underfloor mounted engines with a combined rating of 1,176 kW for a maximum speed of 180 km/h. Acceleration is 1.0 m/sec^2 which reflects the average distance of 25 km between stops. IC3 reduces journey times by an average of 25% with a 44% reduction in operating costs compared with the previous locomotive hauled main line trains.

This train is tailored to the geography and operational requirements of Danish State Railways. An hourly train of five three car sets from Copenhagen leaves one unit behind at the Great Belt. In Fredericia the train splits again, with one unit heading for Sonderborg, one for Esbjerg

170

and the remaining two units for Aarhus. Here the two units separate to serve Struer and Frederikshaven. This is an extreme example of the flexibility of the diesel multiple unit being used to provide through journeys to a wide range of destinations.

Inter-urban services are not the sole province of the DMU. As the British Rail Networker turbo shows, electric standards of performance and reliability can be provided on non-electrified commuter lines at low cost. Services will range from main line operation out of Paddington to the the lightly used suburban routes based on Marylebone station.

Modern DMUs are ideally suited for demonstration services, either in advance of up-grading to electrification or when lines are re-opened. They provide a low cost way of evaluating the commercial response to service improvements. If ridership gains justify electrification, the DMU fleet can be moved on to upgrade another route.

Tilt

Mention has already been made of tilting trains. The adoption of tilt is a commercial decision, in which the cost benefits of journey time reductions of around 20-30%, must be balanced against the increased capital and operating costs plus potential loss of reliability and availability. The capital costs of one-off track realignments must then be compared with the whole life cost of tilting trains on a discounted cash flow basis (see chapter 21).

At the time of writing it is too early for the maintenance costs and reliability to have been demonstrated over a period of years. However, a 10% increase in capital cost could be used for preliminary evaluations.

Rolling Stock

For the planner, the essential considerations are those of capital cost and capacity, and cost per seat is a key parameter. This favours longer vehicles. The logic is simple: each vehicle must have two bogies, two sets of doors and two crash-resistant ends.

Bogies (comprising wheels, axles and primary suspension) represent weight and cost for each seat carried. Thus, each seat in a 26 m long vehicle will share a smaller proportion of this cost and weight than in a 23 m vehicle with fewer seats. A similar effect can be achieved with articulation, where adjacent vehicles share a central bogie at the expense of an inflexible formation.

Similarly, doors and ends represent unproductive space. In the longer vehicle this is a smaller proportion of the total length. Also the cost of systems, such as air conditioning, is spread over more seats. Comparing British Rail's InterCity 225 (23 m vehicles) and InterCity 250 (26 m vehicles) shows an increase in seating from 556 to 640 for similar nine car formations.

Vehicle length is limited by the 'throw over' on curves which could take a vehicle out of gauge. However, modern suspensions, which are more controlled, and a better understanding of dynamic loading gauges have allowed longer vehicles on BR with minimal associated civil engineering work.

Where capacity is critical, and the loading gauge allows, double deck coaches provide an immediate capacity boost. This has been common with commuter stock for many years. With the growth in demand generated by high speed services, railways in both France and Japan have adopted double deck high speed coaches.

Operation

With modern equipment, availability (the proportion of the fleet available for service each day allowing for maintenance and overhauls) will be at least 85% assuming overnight servicing. Diesel stock will have a range of around 1,600 km which means daily refuelling on most services.

Otherwise, daily attention is limited to interior cleaning of passenger trains and a simple safety check. Service intervals continue to extend, with the basic examination now required every three days or better.

A recent development in North American freight haulage may spread to passenger trains, if plans progress for private access to railway services. Known as 'power by the hour', manufacturers supply and maintain locomotive fleets, guaranteeing availability for a specified service. Each locomotive carries the equivalent of an electricity meter and the railway pays a fixed rate for the energy produced by the engine.

With the increasingly complex technology involved in modern passenger stock, manufacturers would prefer to be responsible for the maintenance of their products. 'Seats by the mile', with the cost per seat mile including leasing a train and its maintenance, could be a future development.

Reference

1. Dowling, J. (1991) "Diesels to Meet the High-Speed Challenge", *Modern Rlys*. 48 pp. 466-468.

Note also that Roger writes every month in *Modern Railways* as its Technical Editor.

16. Getting Things Done

Tony M Ridley

Introduction

The various chapters in this book illustrate the complexity of the task of planning passenger railways. This is as nothing compared with the task of implementing those plans. Yet the one depends on the other.

Good planning does not guarantee that a project will be implemented successfully but it is invariably the case that a badly-planned railway will be very difficult, if not impossible, to implement well. What is success? It has frequently been described as the project being built 'on time and within budget'. This is true, but success also requires the railway to operate safely, reliably and economically.

Railways, by their very nature, are technically complex. The description of the Channel Tunnel as "the greatest civil engineering project of the century" may be true but it ignores the fact that the challenge of the project lies much more with the task of putting a very complex railway system successfully in place than with the civil engineering itself.

What distinguishes railways from other technically-complex systems however is that they have so many interfaces with the communities they serve, particularly in urban areas. The siting of a major power station involves both environmental and social issues, but the site itself is relatively self-contained. By contrast a railway 'site' is very long. Consider, for example, Hong Kong Mass Transit Railway, designed to carry 60,000 passengers per hour per direction through one of the densest urban areas in the world, which required open-cut station construction immediately adjacent to shop fronts. Consider also the task of negotiating union agreements for the Tyne and Wear Metro operating over rights-of-way previously owned by British Rail. Parliamentary processes may be convoluted, petitions and objections have to be resolved, and various other legal requirements (such as preserving listed buildings or environmental features (see chapter 18)) may have to be satisfied.

The creation of a new railway is a multi-faceted task, as the controversy over the Channel Tunnel Link has indicated. It involves the planning, design and construction of physical facilities as well as matters of operation, logistics and information systems. But financial and funding issues are fundamental as the Channel Tunnel has indicated. Environmental questions loom large now for any major project as do institutional and organisational issues - witness the task of obtaining Parliamentary powers for new railways and the long-running saga of 'rows' between Eurotunnel and TML, the Channel Tunnel contractors.

The multi-dimensional nature of the task of putting a new railway system in place can be described by a pentagon with its five sides of

- hardware, the conventional engineering task of designing, manufacturing and building physical products by civil, electrical and mechanical engineers

- software, the use of computer and other modern techniques to interface the total system as well as the logistics of building and operating it

- finware, the costing and cost control as well as the funding of the capital and operating costs of the system

- ecoware, the addressing of all the environmental problems and interfaces which arise from imposing a new system in a community

- orgware, the total institutional, general and project management, human resource and public relations task involved.

This is only a shorthand description of a long and complex series of tasks, each of which has to be carried out expertly. The success of the project, however, will ultimately depend upon the extent to which all are brought together.

Politics too are more involved in transport projects than most others and experience with a variety of such projects suggests a number of prerequisites for success (or not, as the case may be):

- political consensus supporting the project
- a clear strategy underlying the project
- easily-obtained right-of-way
- a small tightly-knit team at the planning stage
- a single-minded implementation team
- good timing

This chapter now turns to three examples of complex railway projects where the pentagon and prerequisites were essential to the well-being of the projects. The sections are necessarily brief, but a short bibliography is provided for further reference.

Tyne and Wear Metro

The Tyne and Wear Metro was born out of the Tyne and Wear Transport Study, carried out by local authorities at the end of the 1960s. At just the same time, the Government had produced first a White Paper and then a Parliamentary Bill specifically designed to encourage public transport in the major regional urban areas.

The creation of a political Passenger Transport Authority and professional Passenger Transport Executive produced first a Policy Statement (in effect a statement of strategy), and a political consensus on the way ahead. The Transport Study recommended the creation of a modern, electrified railway system by the use of the existing North Tyne Loop and the line to South Shields, each of which previously provided an inferior diesel service, together with tunnels under Newcastle and Gateshead linked by a bridge over the Tyne.

The Authority and Executive picked up the recommendation immediately, carried out further feasibility studies using only a small planning team, and pressed forward quickly to obtain finance for the project and Parliamentary powers. The timing of the project was ideal since the Government were looking to support a scheme of the sort at the time.

The timing, together with the various actions taken, resulted in the project moving from a line on a map to digging tunnels in only three years. In contrast, Manchester missed out in the early 1970s and had to wait nearly 20 years for a second opportunity with the Metrolink project, now under construction.

Hong Kong Mass Transit Railway

Political consensus was not difficult to achieve in Hong Kong in the 1970s. First, the form of government was conducive to consensus although there was clearly room for disagreement about priorities for investment. But, with the massive influx of population from China having been absorbed and the housing problem successfully alleviated if not solved, it was timely to turn attention to the future problems of mass movement.

The Government's preparation for the project was of the highest order. It used consultants to carry out initial transport studies which justified the scheme following a careful examination of the feasibility of a number of different alignments for parts of the network. It then produced more detailed designs for the initial railway, together with detailed plans for utility diversions and traffic diversions which proved of inestimable value during the construction stage.

There was one major hiccough when the Hong Kong Government agreed a Letter of Intent with the Japanese, who subsequently reneged, under which the railway would have been designed, financed and built. The Government then created the Mass Transit Railway Corporation, run exactly as a private sector body save only for the fact that the single shareholder was the Government itself. It had a powerful Board of two executive and several very experienced non-executive directors.

The railway was designed to carry 60,000 passengers per hour and has recorded more than 80,000. There is now a group of people - planners, engineers, consultants, contractors and others - who consider themselves as part of a Hong Kong 'mafia', and look with pride on their role in the implementation of what is universally acknowledged to have been a very successful project.

Several things need to be said. The Corporation's project team was outstanding, certainly single-minded in its pursuit of completion, but it was not only the supervision of construction that was successful, the commissioning stage and preparation for operation were also soundly based.

However, the Corporation's success would not have been achieved without the excellent preparatory work of the Government and the first-class team spirit which was generated between the corporation and its contractors, based on a well-conceived and effective set of contract documents.

Channel Tunnel

The fact that the Channel Tunnel will link Britain to the Continent for the first time for 8,000 years, and that it has been contemplated for more than 200 years, is enough to put it in the category 'historic'.

But it is as a railway project that we shall examine it. If ever a project 'has everything' then this is it. It has a need to protect the environment from adverse effects. Nearly 20 specialist reports were commissioned on the impact on animal, tree and plant life. In France archaeological investigation uncovered Bronze Age, Roman and medieval treasures. It has two caverns (the crossover tunnels under the Channel) as tall as two double-decker buses. It required the production of no less than half a million tunnel segments on the UK side alone. It employed more than 10,000 workers. It involved the construction (on both sides of the Channel) of terminals which are massive projects in their own right (the terminal areas are 900 acres at Cheriton (Kent) and 1700 acres at Coquelles (France)). All this and the project has to contend with a banking syndicate of more than 200, a number perhaps unsurprising given that the rate of spend reached some £3 million per day.

There were three principal challenges:

- the logistics of tunnelling, keeping up record production rates day after day with vast amounts of spoil to be removed, and hundreds of thousands of segments to be installed

- the design, procurement, installation, commissioning and bringing into operation of an enormously-complex railway system

- the total human resources task of recruiting and managing two groups of staff, one to finance, oversee and operate the project and the other to design and build it and, even more difficult, to have the two organisations to work effectively together when each of them had staff working in both Britain and France.

Each of the three tunnels (service tunnel, running tunnel (North) and running tunnel (South) is some 50km in length. As the construction involves a land tunnel and a marine tunnel on both sides of the Channel for each of the three, there were in fact 12 tunnelling operations in all. When the first breakthrough of the service tunnel took place on 1 December 1990, the British had completed some 31km and French 19km, of which the land tunnels were 8 and 3 km respectively.

The land tunnelling was not easy but the logistics challenge came from the length of the marine tunnels (over 22km for the British and 15km for the French). It had been expected that progress would be greater on the British side since the chalk was known to be much wetter on the French. Indeed, the design of the French tunnel boring machines (TBM) was different from the British. They were more complex in that they could operate both in 'closed mode' where the chalk was very porous and water-bearing (with pressure up to 145 psi), and 'open mode' where not.

The service tunnels (of less than 5m diameter) proceeded first, followed by the larger (over 7m diameter) running tunnels. All three tunnels have now broken through and, at the time of writing, only the French crossover remains to be completed. Tunnelling records have been broken, with progress in excess of 350m in some weeks.

The British TBMs were 200m in length and up to 1300t in weight , but the French ones were heavier yet. Each British marine TBM had a crew of over 40 men, with fitters an electricians as part of the team; the teams worked 8-hour shifts around the clock.

177

The British teams, who ended their tasks so triumphantly, faced all manner of problems in the early days, and it remains a matter of contention between Eurotunnel (the owner) and TML (Trans-Manche Link, the contractor) whether the problems (e.g. a two-mile length of very wet ground; crumbling chalk; overheating of battery-electric trains sealed to resist saline moisture) could have been foreseen. These and other problems emphasise that the boring itself was perhaps the least of the problems. The sheer logistics of the massive operation presented the main challenge.

The introduction of improved ventilation and of diesel locos, together with overall improved maintenance, contributed greatly. The task was to remove a total of more than 4 million cu m of spoil, first by train and then by high-speed conveyor, to be placed in lagoons behind sea walls built at Shakespeare Cliff. The amount of spoil to be removed reached as much as 3000t per hour.

As spoil was being taken out, segments were carried in. At first they were brought in at both the top (crown) and bottom (invert) of the tunnel. The redesign of the scheme to bring all segments in at the bottom improved efficiency and progress, and also contributed to improved safety.

In Hong Kong, the length of the tunnelled stations of the railway were only, at maximum, the distance between stations. For the Channel Tunnel, the length of the marine tunnels not only presented a massive logistics challenge for spoil removal and segment transport, but also for the installation of electrical and mechanical equipment.

Transport engineering is about the movement of people and goods by road, rail, air, sea and pipeline. The Channel Tunnel comprehends a large part of this total picture - people, goods, road and rail. It is in fact two transport systems in one. British Rail and SNCF (French Railways) will run through trains between London and Paris/Brussels and beyond, for both passengers and freight. They have 'bought' half the capacity of the Tunnel. Eurotunnel, who are the owners, will themselves operate shuttle trains between the terminals. They will carry cars, coaches and HGVs on single- and double-deck shuttles, thereby making the transport system truly bi-modal.

So long as tunnels were being built by national teams towards each other, it was possible to employ methods appropriate to each national engineering culture. Once breakthrough has taken place, however, there is only one project. Construction safety regulations which could be different at the beginning have to be brought together, whilst there cannot be two different processes for one railway system.

It is a fact, however, that the culture of railways is much more national than that of other modes - air and car, for example. At the same time, there was no strict precedent for what is being done in engineering terms. Add to that the fact that the original promoters of the system - the ten contractors who now form TML and five bankers - reverted to contracting and banking roles after the system had been specified, and it is clear that the creation of the transport system is inordinately complex.

Eurotunnel, the owner, now has responsibility for the specification and this change is at the root of much of its dispute with TML. It must also obtain the agreement of the Intergovernmental Commission and its Safety Authority before the system can be brought into operation. It is now already preparing for the time when it will operate its shuttles and handle the passage of BR/SNCF trains. This involves a multiplicity of activities including the writing of operating procedures and the recruiting and training of staff (recognising again the different cultural backgrounds from which they will come) (see chapter 13).

TML meanwhile have been designing or overseeing the design of the rolling stock, signalling, control centres, telecommunications, ventilation and other systems. There is a massive procurement task and then the logistics task of installation (perhaps greater that than for the tunnelling itself). All have to be interfaced and the parts, and then the whole, commissioned before handing over to Eurotunnel.

Overlying all this work of engineering, logistics and management looms the question of finance. The sums of money involved have been so large that it has often seemed that, contrary to the happier history in Hong Kong, engineering has had to respond to finance rather than finance being the servant of the project.

References

Railway Gazette International 14b (1990) "Anatomy of a Channel Tunnel".

Ridley, T.M. (1972) "Experience in the Operation of a Passenger Transport Executive", Proceedings, Conference on Transportation Engineering, Thomas Telford, London.

Ridley, T.M. (1973) "Tyneside Rapid Transit", *Traff. Engng. & Ctrl.* 14 .

Ridley, T.M. (1976) "Mass Transit Comes to the Tropics", *Developing Rlys.* 1976, Railway Gazette International.

Ridley, T.M. (1980) "The Hong Kong Mass Movement Miracle", *Transport 1.* "Urban Railways and the Civil Engineer", Proceedings, Institution of Civil Engineers Conference, Thomas Telford, London (1987).

Ridley, T.M. (1988) "Rapid Growth Forces Strategy Rethink", *Developing Metros* 1988, Railway Gazette International.

"The Channel Tunnel", Proceedings, Conference of Institution of Civil Engineers and Societe des Ingenieurs et Scientifiques de France, Thomas Telford, London (1989).

Ridley, T.M. (1990) "Abolishing Barriers - the Channel Tunnel", Annual Convention, Institution of Mining Electrical and Mining Mechanical Engineers, Blackpool.

Muir Wood, A. (1991) "The Channel Tunnel - View of a Teredo", *Tunnelling and Underground Space Technology* 6, Pergamon, London.

Wilson, D. (1991) "Breakthrough - Tunnelling the Channel", Century (in association with Eurotunnel), London.

See also Chapter 8 for a discussion about the alternative routes for Britain's Channel Tunnel Rail Link.

17. Costing Passenger Railways

Don Box

Introduction

A distinction must be drawn between calculating the costs of altering existing rail services and the provision of a completely new railway. The latter will have the advantage of being able to employ the most modern operating techniques, new equipment tailor-made for the service, and other benefits arising from being able to start from a "clean sheet"; on the other hand, it also carries risks with as yet untried equipment and practices, and may be subject to increased safety requirements, as "safety hysteria" is attached to rail services to make them even safer than they already are. Costing an existing rail service, or a modification to one, however, involves the forced retention of unsuitable equipment, and understanding and reflecting the residue of past decisions where these impinge on the future.

There are projects which, although initially appearing to be of the new railway variety, are actually part of a wider railway network. The new Channel Tunnel services, whilst using special purpose-built trainsets, terminals and maintenance facilities, will use track and signalling systems employed extensively (more extensively, in fact) by other services, both passenger and freight (see chapter 8). These various other services will be considerably affected by the new service, and cost implications on these services also need to be taken into account.

Development of Rail Costing Methods

Once railways had established accounting systems to record the costs incurred by the various railway operations, and kept detailed statistics of these and the traffic carried, it was comparatively easy to derive average costs for a particular traffic. For example, average repair costs per train mile require records of labour, materials and other expenditure on train repair, and statistics of train mileage. The most common use of such derivatives is as a measure of comparative cost efficiency: of types of train in the example quoted. The finer the breakdown of cost headings and their matching with appropriate 'workload' statistics, the better the range of average costs available to meet particular situations.

181

The shortcomings of this **average cost** approach are twofold. First, there is no proper recognition of the 'jointness' present in so much railway activity. Joint supply occurs if the production of one service implies the ability to produce others without employing additional resources. For example, the cost of a set of traincrew is joint to the outward and return train services operated, as the abandonment of the return service will not affect the traincrew cost of the network. Secondly, a system for synthesizing the average costs for a railway service is needed, because the significance of the various elements in the total cost (see Table 17.1) can vary between services. Of course, the relative importance of the cost categories also affects the effort expended in determining cost rates for that category.

Cost Category		Annual cost (£M)	%
Train operation	- traincrew	410.1	11.4
	- fuel	171.0	4.7
Train provision	- shunting	15.3	0.4
	- stabling/cleaning	71.7	2.0
	- fuelling/power supply	46.6	1.3
	- other	16.3	0.5
Operations Control	- local management	70.4	2.0
	- control	58.5	1.6
	- signalling	109.9	3.1
Train Maintenance		584.7	16.2
Terminals		379.4	10.5
Commercial (Marketing etc.)		121.6	3.3
Security (Police etc.)		20.0	0.6
Route Infrastructure	- Track	603.4	16.8
	- Signals	170.1	4.7
	- Telecommunications	79.7	2.2
Train Catering		42.3	1.2
General	- Management	207.9	5.8
	- Depreciation etc.	204.0	5.7
	- Miscellaneous	218.9	6.1
TOTAL		3601.8	100.0

(Average £10-£15 per train mile).

Table 17.1 Typical Rail Operating Costs by Activity.
(1991 prices) (Source: 1).

The studies into rail costs undertaken by the British Transport Commission from 1948 led to great advances in understanding the nature of railway costs, and the first system for the routine costing of rail traffic on the British network. The general approach was to consider rail costs as belonging to one or other of three broad categories which reflected the degree of variability or jointness in cost. The first category - direct costs- were those of providing, maintaining and operating the trains; these were considered to vary with traffic levels in the medium term. The indirect costs of track, signalling and administration were considered to be fixed into the long term, and joint to the traffic using the particular facility.

A certain amount of ambiguity arose in the treatment of terminal costs. The loading and unloading of parcels was indisputably a direct cost, but other costs incurred at terminals were more fixed in nature. These latter were therefore classified as "specific indirect costs" because they tended to be invariable to the *level* of traffic, but were specific to the *type* of traffic. This was a useful concept to have when the costs of all the passenger traffic in a given area were considered.

Classifying costs as direct, indirect or specific indirect was a useful framework for reference purposes, but it tended to disguise degrees of variability and jointness within one cost heading. A better way was to consider the physical resources needed to provide the service, and the manner and degree to which these resources were to be used. The problem then reduces to determining the appropriate cost rates for each type of resource, both for their provision and their use. Later developments in costing on British Railways inexorably moved in this general direction.

The Cost Structure of Passenger Train Operations

Passenger train services are planned, timetabled and rostered in great detail. (A roster is a list of the duties to be performed by a particular type of resource over a period of time; trainsets, traincrew etc. are then allocated to perform these rosters). A train service may use resources from several such rosters e.g. locomotives, carriages and traincrew. By analysing the rosters, the proportion of time spent on the service to be costed gives the number of resources of each type used by the service in question. If diesel traction is used, time must also be allowed in the roster for refuelling; all traction types require time for routine servicing and inspection. Moreover, the sequence of duties to be performed must be practical by allowing sufficient 'layover' time between duties.

Present practice tends towards 'dedicated' resources e.g. a fleet of trainsets are exclusively used on a particular service. This makes roster analysis more straightforward, but does not obviate the need for special expertise to determine the number of rosters (and therefore the number of resources) required.

Traincrew rostering presents special problems, as we have seen in chapter 13. Moreover, neither trainsets nor traincrew are available continuously. Trains have to be repaired, and it is for the maintenance engineer to indicate the expected availability of the relevant rolling stock, in the prevailing circumstances, and therefore the 'maintenance spares' to be allocated to the service (usually about 1 in 6).

The resource implications of operating a train service are thus a function of the utilisation of these resources under the local operating conditions, and the restrictions on continuous availability peculiar to each type of resource. However, if the resources are shared by other services, changes in these other services could affect the overall utilisation of those resources and thus the equivalent number debitable to the service being costed. The introduction of the service may improve the utilisation of the common resources, or the withdrawal of a service may worsen resource utilisation. This is a familiar characteristic of **common costs** in a transport system, which can be defined as those costs which vary approximately with the scale of operations. The **incremental costs** of a service are thus the difference in resource requirements for the network as a whole, with and without the service under consideration.

The cost-rate applicable to the number of traincrew determined by roster analysis can normally be obtained from the paybill, but train maintenance cost rates are more difficult to determine. The amount of maintenance necessary will depend upon the technical characteristics of the rolling stock, the standards laid down for safe and reliable operation of the equipment, the intensity of use, commercial requirements for the passenger environment and, of course, the efficiency of the maintenance organisation. Usually, the maintenance engineer will lay down standard procedures for the maintenance of the differing types of rolling stock for which he is responsible. In broad terms, these will dictate the frequency with which inspection, component changing etc. are to be carried out. Given the knowledge of the standard cost of carrying out these maintenance routines, it is a relatively simple matter to derive annual maintenance costs.

So far, we have treated train maintenance costs as time costs i.e. varying with quantity and time in use. However, a given type of rolling stock can be used on services exhibiting quite different conditions (e.g. flat or hilly) and intensities of use (e.g. peak only or all-day), in which case the maintenance costs arising can be quite different to those

184

expected from average use. The practical manifestation of this is that the maintenance work arising from routine inspections and workshop repairs of trainsets can be significantly different from that expected. This effect is often accommodated by introducing a further variable into maintenance costs - a mileage, as well as a time, element.

Maintenance consists of direct labour, materials and workshop or depot overheads. The first is variable (in the medium term) with the maintenance workload, the second more variable still, but the third is dependent upon the utilisation of the workshop and depot facilities, and is fixed over wide ranges of maintenance workload. Thus if the maintenance of trainsets on a new service takes up spare capacity in the workshops its incremental maintenance cost will be less than the average of existing and continuing services. (These considerations only apply to the (usual) situation where railways undertake their own maintenance; the cost of bought-in maintenance will depend upon the contractual arrangements between the two parties).

Some provision must be made in the costs for the eventual replacement of the assets, if the services are to have a long-term future. Remembering that existing services are encumbered by past decisions, the provision for replacement must reflect what will be required (both in scale and quality) when the replacement time comes. Assumptions about the rolling stock to be employed on individual services must be consistent with the long-term strategies of the railway (e.g. electrification). The replacement cost is a joint cost over the life of the asset in useful service (see Table 17.2), which may include employment on services other than that for which it was originally designed. If the service is being costed as a flow of costs and benefits over time, then the replacement cost will be inserted at the appropriate time. Otherwise, the replacement cost may be expressed as an annual renewal provision, taking into account the expected life of the asset, which may differ from the 'accounting' life.

Asset Type	Asset Life (years)
Track	15-50 depending upon use
Signalling	30
Locomotives	25
Electric Multiple Units	30
Passenger Carriages	25
High Speed Trains	20

Table 17.2 Typical Lives of Passenger Railway Assets. (Estimated)

185

Fuel costs complete the catalogue of train operating costs. Diesel fuel is a straightforward matter of determining fuel consumption of different sizes of train under various operating conditions. Electric traction is more complicated, as electric power authorities usually operate multi-part tariffs, differentiating between peak and offpeak consumption (making the costs both fixed and variable). It is usual to treat lineside traction equipment (e.g. the overhead lines, conductor rails, substations etc.) as part of the railway infrastructure, as its cost structure is akin to that of the track.

Infrastructure Costs
Railways differ from other modes of transport in that they usually provide their own infrastructure (track, signalling and terminals) (but see chapter 10 for exceptions). In any case, railway ownership does not affect the basic cost structure.

Fig. 17.1 Austrian freight at Brenner. Freight trains are able to use passenger railway capacity at marginal costs.

Each of the four main elements of infrastructure - route structures, track, signalling and terminals - exhibit jointness to varying degrees, and will therefore be dealt with separately. The principal and pervasive

186

difference between train operating costs and infrastructure costs arises from the large difference in divisibility of costs. Infrastructure comes in large 'steps', much of which, in consequence, remains unused (for example, in the form of train paths not taken up).

Route structures (e.g. embankments, tunnels, bridges, boundary walls and fences) are almost entirely joint to the train services using the route. Adding or taking away a service will not normally affect their costs, except where an additional service requires the route to be widened.

The measurement of *track* costs, either in total or as an assessment of incremental cost resulting from an additional service, will be dependent upon the inspection and maintenance routines of the track maintenance engineer. These will, in turn, depend upon common safety standards, the kinds of materials used and technical specification of the track, the commercial requirements of the train service (for comfort, reliability etc.) and the weight, type and speed of trains passing over it. These factors are usually subsumed into a track categorization system, and the average cost of maintaining a mile of plain track in each category worked out by reference to the type and frequency of maintenance routines required to be applied to it. Additional, faster and heavier traffic (including freight - see Fig. 17.1) will result in a raising of the track quality to a higher, more expensive level. The cost difference between the two track categories (i.e. before and after the introduction of the new service) is therefore part of the incremental cost of that traffic, and can be relatively small where, for instance, a 'local' passenger service is added to a high-speed line.

Incremental track cost also includes the additional facilities required by the new service (e.g. additional track to provide the extra train paths required, switches (points) to gain access to station platforms, carriage sidings etc.). These additional facilities will also have a maintenance category, dependent upon the type, speed and amount of traffic passing over them.

Local circumstances, however, can cause significant deviations from the average cost of a particular track category, as is shown by the figures for new construction in Table 17.3. Variations may be due to access difficulties for maintenance purposes because of the sheer intensity of the train service, the presence of tunnels on the route, and/or bad ground conditions.

Provision for the replacement of track used by a new service can also be dealt with through the avoidable/incremental approach. A change in track use (whether it is more, faster or heavier traffic) results in a reduction in the 'life' of the track, and therefore more frequent renewals or an increase in the annual provision for renewal. The difference between the annual renewal provision before and after the change gives the means of imputing an incremental renewal cost to the new service.

	no. of tracks	
	single	double
Track only (£M per mile)		
Complete renewal on existing formation	0.5	1
Route inc. track and signals (£M per mile)		
Flat countryside, cheap land	3	5
Hilly countryside, expensive land	8	16
Elevated	10	20
Cut-and-cover tunnel	15	30
Deep bore tunnel	30	50
Stations (£M each)		
2-car unstaffed wooden halt with bus shelter	0.1	0.3
2-car unstaffed elevated halt with bus shelter	0.6	0.8
4-car staffed concrete halt with brick shelter	0.5	1
10-car InterCity without facilities	-	5
10-car InterCity with facilities	-	10
2-car underground tram stop	10	15
8-car underground 'heavy' rail station (inc. alternative emergency exit)	-	50
Rolling Stock (£M each)		
Main-line Locomotives	2	
2-car Multiple Units	1	
Trams/Light Rail articulated Vehicles	1	
Main-line Passenger Coaches	0.3	

Table 17.3 Typical Capital Costs.
(at 1991 prices) (see also refs. 2 & 3.)

Signalling costs present problems of quite a different order, and generalization is difficult. If a new service requires additional track facilities, then it is likely that commensurate additional signalling equipment will also be needed. This additional equipment will have to be compatible with that which is already *in situ*, and could, therefore, be of a higher standard than that which would be demanded by the additional service in isolation. Also, the existing signalling system may be of insufficient capacity to accommodate the additional service, in which case a complete reconstruction of the signalling on the route may be necessary.

Signalling systems require signalbox staff and traffic controllers. Present day technology, with signalling centres controlling large parts of the network, means that only major additions to the system are likely to require additional signalling staff.

As already noted, trackside electric traction equipment is treated as part of infrastructure. Putting an additional service on an already-electrified line will only incur additional electrification costs if the additional electrical load imposed by the new service necessitates a strengthening of the existing system (e.g. with more sub-stations). Otherwise, only the elements added to the network need to be considered as part of the incremental cost of the new service.

Terminal costs are similar. The costs of newly-opened stations (including their staffing) are part of the incremental cost of a new service, as are extensions to the facilities of existing stations, or extended opening times. In many cases, the introduction of new services will merely improve the utilisation of existing terminal facilities.

Administration costs are difficult to quantify, both in their significance as a separate cost category (there have been many changes to the definition of 'administration') and in their variability (or otherwise) with train service provision. Some elements, such as the direct management of resources, will tend to vary, but only major increases or decreases in the scale of service provision are likely to have an impact. Likely to be far more significant are organisational changes, changes in the geographical 'spread' of activity, or the introduction of completely new groups of services e.g. international passenger services through the Channel Tunnel.

Summary

It is clear that only in rare circumstances will the incremental costs of a new service coincide with the average costs of existing services. Moreover, the incremental costs of services can vary substantially, depending upon the existence or otherwise of spare capacity in the system. The determination of the costs of a new service will start by identifying where spare capacity exists, and whether any part of it can be utilised for the new service. This will be followed by the determination of what new resources are required, and then the cost of providing and using these new resources (as well as the existing ones) will be calculated.

In principle, there is little difference in the approach adopted for train services and for the infrastructure upon which they run. In practice, however, the proximity of average and incremental costs for train services has led to a tacit acceptance of their equality in some circumstances. For infrastructure, the wide disparity between average and incremental cost, and early difficulties in measuring incremental cost, has resulted in the development of different measurement techniques.

There has been, until now, no mention of **marginal costs**, defined as the increase in cost resulting from the last unit of output, since it is difficult to define in the rail context. Does one want to measure the marginal cost of a passenger seat-mile, or a train-mile? Is the network of track and terminals to be considered as fixed over the range of output within which the change in marginal costs is to be measured? If infrastructure facilities are variable, there will be 'steps' in the total cost curve as extensions to the network are brought in. If the network is fixed, there will be limits on the number of train-miles that can be accommodated. Nevertheless, within these limits, a total cost curve can be built up from the costing of successive increases in the train service. Marginal cost is the slope of this cost curve and will, of course, vary with train miles or other unit of output.

Incremental or avoidable cost can be considered as practical manifestations of marginal cost. As concepts, the former have the advantages of being associated with a stated practical change in service provision, and can accommodate cost headings, such as track, signalling and terminals, characterised by large capacity 'steps'.

It is customary to classify rail operating costs under the headings of traincrew, fuel, ticket sales, track maintenance, etc. Categorization of such cost headings as specific or joint, and application of a pre-determined formula for the treatment of all costs in each category, before examination of the local circumstances, can seriously mislead. It is better to treat the concepts of specific, common or joint, variable or fixed costs as a convenient shorthand notation to summarize the expected behaviour of costs in a local situation, after research into that local situation has been completed. It follows that a good understanding of railway engineering and operating and their cost implications is essential to successful planning.

Various mathematical techniques have been developed to model the behaviour of rail costs under the impact of varying levels of service provision. But these must depend upon a proper understanding of railway costs to be successfully adopted for a particular planning problem, which is why the emphasis here has been upon practicalities, rather than on theoretical techniques.

References

1. British Rail Board (1991) "Annual Report and Accounts 1990-1991".
2. Harris, N.G. (1988) "Dependence on the Past", *Mod. Rlys.* 45 pp. 309-311.
3. Passenger Transport Executive Group (PTEG) (1988) "Light Rapid Transit Report", App. 3, Avon, RTPI, LRTA.

The International Union of Railways (UIC) have produced a number of publications on the development and application of costing methods within a mainly-European environment. Of particular relevance are "Principles and Methods for Rail Transport Costing" (code 374R, 3rd ed. 1/10/1977) and "Rail Transport Costing, Passenger Traffic Costs, Study of the Laws of Their Variation" (code 378R, 2nd ed. 1/1/1984).

The development of techniques in Britain was first described in the British Transport Commission's Annual Report for 1951, subsequently analysed in considerable detail in the "Report to the Joint Steering Group of the Ministry of Transport & British Railways Board on Costing, Budgetary Control & Management Information in British Railways" (Cooper Brothers & Co., 1966). A later booklet "Measuring Cost & Profitability in British Railways" (BRB, 1978) described and analysed the development of various costing techniques (including the avoidable cost approach) up to that time.

See also:

Beesley, M. & Kettle, P. (1985) "Improving Railway Financial Performance" (Gower).

Joy, S. (1989) "Railway Costs and Planning", Jnl. Trans. Econ. & Pol. 23 pp. 45-54.

Waters, W.G. II (1985) "Rail Cost Analysis", ch. 5 pp. 101-135 in Button, K.J. & Pitfield, D.E. "International Railway Economics" (Gower).

18. Railways and the Environment

Stuart Cole

Introduction
The environment when discussed in relation to transportation conjures up visions of six lane motorways, cutting through communities, encircling city centres, dominating urban areas and ruining rural tranquillity. The vision extends to high volumes of traffic causing noise and pollution. Rarely is the impact of railways immediately brought to mind but the consideration of environmental issues in relation to railway infrastructure construction is not new[14].

Current plans for railway development include the construction of the Channel Tunnel Rail Link (CTRL) through Kent, the Jubilee Line extension in urban London and the TGV Sud Est extension through Provence. Attached to all has been the realisation that: -

a) they will bring travel benefits;
b) they may reduce road traffic flows especially in the short term and thus bring environmental benefits; but
c) there is a need to minimise the adverse environmental impact during both construction and operation of the new services.

Construction of these projects already includes reference to past experience (e.g. with TGV Atlantique, and see chapter 16). First, however, it is necessary to be clear about what the environment is, and what effects railway construction and operation have on it.

Definition of the Environment by the Resident
There are two situations where residents can be affected by railways. First, there is the adverse effect of the construction of a new railway line such as the CTRL, whilst secondly, there is the effect of increasing traffic flows on an existing line. Adverse effects may be caused by noise, visual intrusion, vibration, air pollution or community severance. The value of adverse environmental effects to householders could be based on how much money the affected residents would need to receive in order for them to consider themselves no worse off.

If a person is moved from a house because of a new railway development, the owner of the house loses the right to use that property and this right is transferred to the railway operator. In exchange (s)he receives a sum of money (usually the market value), which is clearly to compensate for the loss of property rights. If the occupier is to be no worse off than before, the amount of money received must equal the valuation of that right. From this property right (i.e. the right to use the house) can be derived the idea of 'amenity right' (i.e. the right to a peaceful and quiet environment).

Perception of Residents Next to the Line

The issue of definition leads onto the question of perception of the environment. Research[3,12] has indicated that social class is a major causal variable in the value individuals attach to the environment. On the macro scale this is probably evident in the response to plans to provide new high speed rail links in Europe. The Channel Tunnel Rail Link through Kent and the TGV Sud Est extension through the Aix en Provence area north of Marseilles are primarily through areas of wealthy professional and business people or well-established prosperous farmers who do not see a benefit from the TGV or the line either directly or indirectly. They do not see it as a benefit that exceeds the impact on their property, business interests or lifestyle. Objections on environmental grounds are well articulated and supported by local politicians.

These views of the new line can be compared with demands by Wales, Scotland and the north of England and the north east of France for high speed trains, passenger stations and freight yards. Here the environmental impact is no doubt perceived, but the economic benefits are seen as being greater.

Therefore although the environmental elements may be the same and although each may vary in the degree of impact, the level of acceptance through a trade off between environment and economics will vary considerably.

Environmental Elements - A Detailed Discussion

The environmental effect of a project is only one of several effects. There will also be effects on the use of resources, and on the opportunity cost of using resources for one project against another. Any evaluation of the environmental impact must be consistent with the total evaluation of the project, and although this does not necessarily mean that each component must be evaluated in the same units, it does mean that the form of evaluation has to permit a comparison of the various impacts and consequences of the construction. If, for example, noise is measured in one way and visual intrusion in another then an inter-comparison of the two is very difficult.

The forms of environmental pollution resulting from railway locomotives or power units and from the track that carries them may be divided broadly into two categories. First, there are those forms that are consequent upon the traffic flow including noise, pollution and vibration; and secondly, there are those environmental impacts resulting from the structure and include visual intrusion, ecological, landscape and heritage effects, land take and changes in land access[7].

Excessive noise involves both the social penalties of a poor environment and the economic disadvantages caused by reduced efficiency. Over the last thirty years road traffic has become the predominant form of transport in Britain, and the consequent noise problem is widespread[9].

Fortunately, in railway working the air polluting effects of steam traction have been largely removed. Diesel operation, however, does produce higher levels of air pollution than electric traction. In any event the pollution causes annoyance, whilst at worst it can constitute a health hazard. In addition, dust is produced by vehicles travelling on the railway (e.g. from brake blocks), the vibration of buildings and their contents are often caused by the movement of heavy traffic (particularly freight trains) over irregularities in the permanent way.

Noise

Noise is a highly subjective element and so the degree of annoyance will vary between individuals. Social surveys have shown that dissatisfaction towards noise expressed by people in their homes depends on the level and on the variability of the noise.

Methods for predicting of railway noise are dealt with in chapter 19. Typical of these methods were the techniques suggested by those local authorities in discussion with British Rail in respect of the CTRL[13]. These showed the relationship between noise and the number of trains on the route, train speed, distance from the line and age of rolling stock, under a variety of freight and passenger traffic types and conditions. Noise data are collected for a particular scheme, and a measure is taken of the numbers of people and numbers of sensitive properties; e.g. houses, schools and hospitals, within each noise range band. By plotting the distribution of numbers of people in each noise band, an analysis of the effects can be made.

Vibration

A more detailed account of vibration and its effects and measurement are contained in chapter 19, but may be categorised into human and structural. The effects of vibration on the human body that can be caused by train pass-bys include a reduced ability to get information through sight, information processing and speech. But the effects of vibration on task performance are dependent on the nature of the tasks and thus not easily quantifiable. There is also limited information on the relationship between vibration and health. There might also be discomfort (i.e. unpleasant sensations within the body) caused by frequent train pass-bys.

Structural damage may be induced by railway operations, e.g. building vibration and the rattling of loose glazing, while in extreme cases damage can be caused to the structure of a building, particularly one of great age. Normally the levels of vibration are much higher than the levels that are perceptible or annoying to humans.

Air Pollution

The techniques for measuring pollution in the atmosphere are not as advanced as those for noise. The impact from electric traction is small, especially when compared with road traffic effects.

Visual Intrusion

A further environmental impact on residents, resulting from the construction of a new railway is visual intrusion caused by the structure. This includes the loss of privacy caused by rail users seeing inside houses and gardens, the effects on the quality of life within visual distance of a major civil engineering structure, the effects of the line and trains on the general scene, and the loss of character or setting of historic buildings (where the breaching of Chester City walls by the North Wales main line is an example)[9]. Quantifying this effect has, however proved difficult[2,7].

Both the landscape and the residents of an area must be protected from unreasonable visual intrusion. For example, the effects on non-users should be assessed through the extent to which the railway is blended into the natural topography by selection of the most appropriate horizontal and vertical alignment, the degree of screening of elevated sections of line by natural vegetation or landscaping, the extent to which it is blended into the general vista through the use of cuttings, the integration of at-grade sections with greenbelts and parks, and the extent to which "planning blight" is prevented.

Visual intrusion may also be caused by the siting of sidings and stationary rolling stock at those locations. The construction of passing loops, sidings, freight yards and maintenance depots should be subject to intrusion controls to protect the external visible environment of localised areas in towns and villages. The zoning of housing, recreational and landscape or ecologically sensitive sites should be considered when providing planning permission or Parliamentary powers for the construction of rail operating facilities.

A considerable amount of discussion based on subjective views will however often take place in respect of these opposing objectives. Judgments on visual intrusion may be helped by visual aids, such as models and photographic techniques. They can be used at public inquiries to help to increase public understanding of the project.

Community Severance

The concept of severance is defined by Lassier[10] as the responses in terms of behaviour, attitudes and perceptions of a community to the presence of a "lined" feature in a rural area that prevents or restricts communications across it. This type of feature developed over the last two hundred years as canals, railways, roads, and more recently, motorways. One obvious consequence is the extra travel time resulting from diversions to a reduced number of crossing points.

The impact of severance on a community may be proved in a variety of ways. The severance or disturbance of established neighbourhoods can have both cultural and psychological consequences. A large variety of patterns and services, such as shopping patterns, and school attendance areas, can be upset by physical severance, thus breaking up integrated neighbourhoods.

Some neighbourhoods have cultural groups that may be symbolised by strong family connections while others comprise residential areas of homogeneous social classes complete with supporting educational and social institutions. These may be divided by the railway. A scheme may have serious consequences upon the "sense of neighbourhood". The evaluation of the importance of neighbourhood objectives in relation to those of the community needs to be determined by formal survey and analysis techniques, or by discussion between planners and residents.

In the present state of knowledge the aims of severance analysis are limited to estimating the number of people affected and the form and severity of the effects. The assessment produced is qualitative. There are many factors[13] to which the degree of severance may be related:-
a) location of the home in relation to the major crossing points;
b) the presence or absence of pedestrian crossing facilities;

c) individual characteristics of the residents such as age, sex, length of residence, social class;
d) the distribution of facilities such as shops, school, pubs, churches etc., on either side of the railway;
e) the socio-economic mix of the population;
f) the alternate locational availability of housing.

It has been suggested that severance is a short term effect and that shopping, educational and other patterns affected by a new railway scheme will adjust to this new development and a new social structure and new lines of communication within the community will eventually develop.

Land Take

Land take is another aspect of the environment that cannot be physically measured on its own but is an integral part of the environmental framework. However, all transport infrastructure schemes (railways, roads, airports, seaports) inevitably consume land that is a non renewable and scarce resource. Because of the high degree of competition for land it is likely that most land currently used for transport has previously been used for another economic purpose, e.g. agriculture, leisure. It may have non-economic definable qualities as a Site of Special Scientific Interest (SSSI), an Area of Outstanding Natural Beauty (AONB), or be otherwise ecologically significant. It is therefore insufficient to consider the use of land for railway purposes purely in terms of area. There is also the consideration of the opportunity cost of the other uses that may conflict with the objectives of an efficient transport system. In addition, there are the effects on historic and cultural sites that should be restored or preserved. Although the impact will not be quantifiable it may be significant.

In an inter-urban rail scheme (e.g. the CTRL or TGV routes), agricultural land usually predominates in land take. It should be possible to improve on the current methods used to express the effects of land take. This can be done by replacing the measurement in hectares of agricultural land by grade, with a table of values expressing the food producing capacity of the land, in terms of its value to the economy. This would provide a monetary measure for the opportunity cost of agricultural land used for rail construction purposes. Any monetary valuation of this output will be sensitive to agricultural policies related to guaranteed prices or subsidies.

Land with special status should be identified; some of this land may have a statutory protection order, but any other land without protection, and having considerable environmental or historical significance, should be included. There are occasionally benefits to be derived from land take by railway construction works such as the use of spoil from worked-out mineral areas or waste heaps, thus enabling such areas to be cleared. For example coal slag heaps in Nord-Pas de Calais region were removed to provide the base for the TGV Nord.

Heritage and Conservation Areas
Protection is required for such cases if sustainable development is to be achieved. Elements to consider include:

a) man-made structures (ancient monuments, listed buildings, conservation areas etc.);
b) areas of land-form, vegetation of wildlife habitat (National Park, AONB, Nature Reserve, etc.);
c) other landforms, buildings or habitats having historic, scientific or amenity value (common land, town and village greens, allotments, etc.);
d) ecological factors including features not otherwise protected or designated, e.g. valleys, meadows, woodland, heath, hedges, etc.;
e) disruption due to construction; and
f) view from the railway.

Railways in Transport Policy

As environmental issues assume greater importance, there have been calls for greater railway development, since rail is less environmentally damaging than some other modes (notably road). For instance, the Council for the Protection of Rural England (CPRE) in submissions to Parliament[5] and to the Government[6], suggested a shift in transport policy. They suggested a move away from a policy of supporting roads as underpinning economic growth, to one of active protection for the environment in line with sustainable development principles, taking into account the needs and concerns of the wider environment. Local communities and the protection of the countryside need to be considered as well as the claimed needs of the traveller in current policies.

However, in Britain, there seems little likelihood of railways forming a major part of inter-urban passenger transport policy. Even in urban areas, large scale investment approval has been limited to London. The scope for encouraging greater use of trunk railways for passenger (and freight) traffic is not explored in any depth under the current system. "Roads for Prosperity"[8] dismisses rail options in asserting that: " . . .even with the continued expansion of rail, it cannot take other than a small part of the increase in total demand for transport. Road and rail mostly serve different markets, and for most traffics the one cannot be substituted for the other."

In contrast to other countries, British Rail InterCity passenger services are not subsidised by government, but are required to make a profit. Although a minimal amount of grant (only £4 million in 1989/90 providing finance for just six schemes[1]) is available under Section 8 of the Railways Act 1974 "for rail freight handling facilities to help keep lorries off unsuitable roads", no such equivalent exists for inter-urban passenger services.

Railways are considered narrowly as an 'option for relieving congestion' in the White Paper[8]. Nevertheless, the relative benefits of railways vis-a-vis roads include:

a)   a much better safety record;
b)   much less land take for infrastructure;
c)   potentially less visual and noise intrusion;
d)   no atmospheric pollution along the route of electrified lines; and
e)   more efficient use of energy and alternatives to fossil fuel, e.g. Hydro Electric Power.

The current British system lacks scope for evaluating the modal split along the routes where new or upgraded roads have been proposed in the trunk road programme. For example, the proposal to upgrade the A1 to motorway standard was announced in July 1990 without any consideration of the scope for upgrading the East Coast Main Line, which follows a parallel route between London and Edinburgh. Early planning work for the Oxford - Birmingham corridor showed that while electrification of the railway had a positive Benefit:Cost ratio (see chapter 21), it was not financially worthwhile; the M40 motorway was built as it only required a positive Benefit : Cost ratio.

An Environmental Assessment Framework

Environmental assessments are becoming an accepted part of planning for new rail lines. That for LUL's Jubilee line[11] is required to identify (a) the the nature and scale of environmental effects likely to result from the construction and operation of the line, and (b) what measures should be taken to minimise those effects. issues are normally considered under two broad headings of (i) during construction, and (ii) after completion.

The development of an environmental framework applies to all new linear transport construction - both road and rail. Strategic guidance should be formulated for those rail routes identified as necessary to relieve congestion on alternative road routes, or in creating a high speed rail network.

It is essential to take a view of the complete scheme (as has been done for the Channel Tunnel Rail Link), thus providing a wide ranging analysis and more creative and sensitive solutions. In a recent report[4] the idea of a Trunk Route Environmental Brief (TREB) was proposed as providing this facility. This new approach would provide a framework to summarise the major land use and environmental constraints. The framework would enable the Department of Transport to generate alternative proposals for passenger and freight transport along the trunk route or corridor under consideration. The implications of each solution could then be tested in relation to a set of environmental criteria. The framework would establish the opportunities and constraints as a starting point to formulate possible solutions to the problem of congestion along trunk routes. It is no longer acceptable to assume that forecast demand for road and rail traffic should be accommodated simply by creating additional capacity; indeed, this is no longer held as sensible in urban areas.

The next stage would therefore be the generation of alternatives that examine fully the possibility of traffic management and rail investment as well as motorway construction. If new railways (or roads) are to be built or existing lines upgraded the suggested routes should be examined in the light of the Environmental Brief. Because decision makers would be presented with a range of strategic options, the advantages and disadvantages of each proposal would be evaluated.

Conclusions

The growing concern with the environmental consequences of road construction will apply itself to new railway lines and to lines whose upgrading results in increased usage especially at night and for freight.

The compensation element is clearly very important for landowners and householders, but is generally well dealt with. The other aspects of environmental concern - those of landscape, access and ecology - are equally important if sustainable development is to be achieved.

The evaluation process must therefore involve the qualitative assessment of schemes with regard to a check-list of environmental objectives. These may be of regional, national or international significance. The judgmental criteria should include the need to minimise:

a) atmospheric pollution;
b) noise/vibration;

c) visual intrusion;
d) severance;
e) land take;
f) damage to the natural environment; and
g) damage to archaeological sites and historic landscapes.

References
1. BRB (1990), British Railways Board, Annual Report 1989-1990, London.
2. Buchanan C. (1963), Traffic in Towns, HMSO, London
3. Cole, S. (1982) A Cost Benefit Approach to Environmental Evaluation of Transport Expenditure, (MSc Thesis) University of Salford, England
4. Cole, S. & Shaw, S. (1992), Environmental Evaluation of Transport Infrastructure, Council for the Protection of Rural England, London.
5. CPRE (1989), "Roads for the Future", Submission of the Council for the Protection of Rural England to the House of Commons. Select Committee Inquiry, House of Commons, London
6. CPRE (1990), "Structure Plans and Regional Planning Guidance", a response by the Council for the Protection of Rural England to the Government's draft Planning Policy Guidance note.
7. DTp (1983), Manual of Environmental Appraisal, Trunk Road Schemes, Department of Transport, London, England.
8. DTp (1990), "Roads to Prosperity", White Paper, CM693, HMSO, London.
9. Jefferson (1976), Route Location with regard to environmental issues. Report of a working party, Department of the Environment, London.
10. Lassier, A. (1976), The environmental evaluation of transport plans. Department of the Environment Research Report 8, London.
11. London Underground Limited (1990), Jubilee Line Extension, Environmental Assessment, Environmental Resources Limited (ERL), London.
12. Maltby, D. (1990) Response to Standing Advisory Committee on Trunk Road Appraisal, University of Salford, England.
13. Sevenoaks (1989), Proposed Channel Tunnel Rail Link, Report on an alternative scheme in which the link is contained in Tunnel to the Medway, Sevenoaks District Council, Sevenoaks, Kent and Howard Humphreys & Partners/D.R. Culverwell, Consulting Engineers.
14. The Times (1935) Great Western Progress 1835-1935, David & Charles, Netwon Abbot, England.

For those wishing to pursue research or are particularly interested in Railways and the Environment the following further references may be of help:

15. EC 1988 European Community Directive 85/337 Environmental Assessment of Major Transport Infrastructure Schemes.
16. House of Commons (1987), Report of the Joint Select Committee on Private Bill Procedure (HC625: Session 1987-88), London.

17. DOE/Welsh Office (1989). The implementation regulations are as follows:
a) Town and Country Planning (Assessment of Environmental Effects) Regulation Statutory Instrument No. 1199, July 1988.
b) Council of Europe directive on the assessment of the effects of certain public and private projects on the environment (85/337 EC) OJEC 5-7-85.
c) Department of the Environment, London; Swyddfa Gymreig (Welsh Office), Caerdydd/Cardiff: Joint Circular on Environmental Assessment 15/88.
d) Department of the Environment, London; Swyddfa Gymreig/Welsh Office, Caerdydd/Cardiff: A Guide to the Procedures, HMSO 1989.
18. The MVA Consultancy/Transecon International: Rail Traffic Forecasts for the Fixed Channel Link, November 1985.
19. The MVA Consultancy: Channel Tunnel Rail Passenger Forecasts Model Development and Scenario Testing, August 1987.
20. SETEC Economie and Wilbur Smith Associates: Eurotunnel Traffic and Revenue Forecasts, June 1988.
21. Steer Davies and Gleave Ltd./Maunsell: Independent Assessment of Rail Services in Kent between London and the Channel Tunnel, January 1989.
22. Channel Tunnel Train Services: BR Study report on long term route and terminal capacity: British Railways Board, July 1988.
23. Cole, S. (1990), Evidence to the Select Committee on the British Railways (No.3) Bill, June 1990, House of Lords, London.
24. Railfreight Distribution (1989), Channel Tunnel Freight Policy Statement, British Rail, London.
25. Keeping TGV Green (1991), International Railway Journal, February 1991, London.
26. SNCF (1991), TGV and the Environment, Press Release 2 August 1991, French Railways, London.
27. Department of Transport (1991), Railway Noise and the Insulation of Dwellings, HMSO, London.

19. Planning for Noise and Vibration

Ben Thanacanamootoo

Introduction
Noise and vibration are by-products of all rail systems and are another form of environmental pollution, even if not in the same way as lead and hydrocarbons are to road traffic. This fact is well established in that, nowadays, environmental impact studies (including noise and vibration) are part of virtually all significant rail projects in the developed world (see chapter 18).

It is economically infeasible and technically impossible to build noiseless rail systems, although rubber-tyred systems such as Lyons' VAL are extremely quiet. However, it is possible and practical to keep the total community noise exposure from rail operations well below that created by most other modes of transport, such as road traffic and aircraft. Since noise and vibration are not generally seen as directly related to the economics and efficiency of a rail system operation, they can be often neglected until problems develop. It is then that the efficiency and economics of including the control of noise and vibration in the planning and design process become apparent, since solutions to mitigate problems not anticipated can be costlier and still not as effective as if they were carried out during construction.

In designing new rail systems, acceptable noise and vibration levels have to be set. Obviously, very restrictive criteria would be costly to achieve and, in some cases, impossible to fulfil. On the other hand, no standards at all or ones that are too lenient can result in nuisance and perhaps in strong community reaction.

Important Acoustical Concepts
Characteristics of Sound: Sound is defined as any variation in pressure that the human ear can detect. The number of pressure variations per second is called the **frequency** of the sound, which is measured in cycles per second or Hertz (Hz). The range of human hearing extends from approximately 20Hz to 20KHz, while the range from the lowest to the highest note of a piano is 27.5 Hz to 4186 Hz.

The **speed** of sound is the rate at which sound waves travel. At a temperature of 20°C, the speed of sound in air is approximately 344 m/s. A sound is made up a number of frequencies, and a sound which is comprised of a single frequency is called a pure tone. The motion of a pure tone can be represented by a sine wave (see Figure 19.1), and is known as a single harmonic motion.

The **wavelength** of a sound is the physical distance from the crest of one wave to the next. Wavelength λ (in metres) is related to frequency f (in Hertz) and the speed of sound c (in metres/second) by the equation:

$\lambda f = c$

A sound wave has also an amplitude A, which is the maximum value of the sinusoidal wave, and a time period T as shown in Figure 19.1.

The Decibel: The unit of measurement of sound pressure is the Pascal (Pa), where 1 Pa is equal to 1 Newton per square metre. Since the weakest sound that an average person can hear at 1000Hz is about $20\mu Pa$ (20×10^{-6} Pa), and the threshold of pain occurs at a sound pressure of approximately 10^8 Pa, the measurement of sound pressure in Pascal would lead to the use of large and unwieldy numbers. Additionally, the ear responds to acoustic stimuli not linearly but logarithmically. For these reasons a logarithmic scale, the decibel (dB), is used to express acoustic measurements and is be defined as

$$\text{Sound Pressure Level } L_p = 10\log_{10}\left(\frac{P}{P_o}\right)^2 = 20\log_{10}\left(\frac{P}{P_o}\right)$$

where p is the sound pressure being measured, Po is the reference sound pressure of 20 μPa.

The decibel scale thus reduces the dynamic range of sound pressure to a more manageable range of sound pressure levels of 0dB to 120dB, zero indicating the reference minimum threshold and 120 the approximate threshold of pain. Since the decibel is a logarithmic scale, normal addition or subtraction cannot be carried out directly. Instead, when two sound levels are combined (or subtracted) they must be added logarithmically. Hence:

$$A \text{ dB} + B \text{ dB} = 10 \log \left(\text{antilog}\left(\frac{A}{10}\right) + \text{antilog}\left(\frac{B}{10}\right)\right)$$

Doubling the number of sources, for example two sound levels of 60 dB, therefore raises the sound pressure level by 3 dB to 63 dB and not 120 dB.

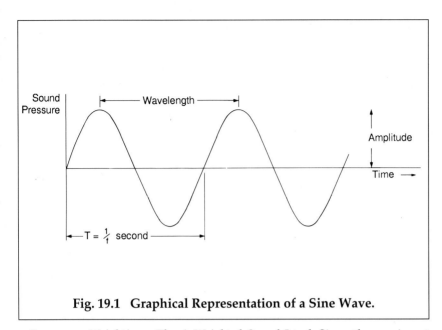

Fig. 19.1 Graphical Representation of a Sine Wave.

Frequency Weighting - The A Weighted Sound Level: Since the ear is not equally sensitive at all sound frequencies, it is essential that this frequency discrimination is taken into account when measuring noise. To obtain measurements from an instrument which purports to represent the response of the ear to noise, so-called frequency-weightings are incorporated in noise-measuring instruments.

There are four weightings included in standard sound level meters, A, B, C and D, although all four are not normally built into a single instrument. The A - weighting is used almost exclusively to assess transport and community noise, to specify emission limits and to set community noise standards throughout the world. It is common practice to append the appropriate letter after the unit symbol as a reminder of the weighting being employed; for example dBA, dBB etc.

Indicators for Railway Noise: Noise from railway operations is characterised by a number of factors which include train frequency, speed of travel, and therefore duration and magnitude of the noise, types of train using the route, rail type and alignment. It is not possible to derive one indicator that can take into account all the characteristics, and hence a family of indicators is used to describe railway noise. The following are the most commonly used measures for railway noise assessment:

- The maximum noise level, L_{Amax}

L_{Amax} is the maximum reading given by a sound level meter and gives an indication of the loudest noise produced. The measurements are repeated many times to obtain a representative value for the maximum noise level. Where maximum noise levels are defined, they are normally based on the noise emission from trains under controlled conditions, excluding noise from other sources.

For night time, L_{Amax} is sometimes used in conjunction with train frequency as an indicator of noise nuisance. This is normally stated as the number of trains causing noise levels equal to or exceeding L_{Amax}.

- The equivalent continuous sound level, L_{Aeq}

The equivalent continuous sound level is defined as the level of a (hypothetical) steady sound that, over the period of measurement, has the same amount of acoustical energy as does the actual time varying sound. Using this measure, fluctuating noise levels, such as would be associated with railway noise, can be described in terms of a single sound level over the same exposure period. Hence, when quoting L_{Aeq}, it is necessary to quote the time period over which the measurement applies. For example, if the time period is 24 hours the equivalent noise level is usually denoted as $L_{Aeq,24hr}$. L_{Aeq} is widely accepted and used as a measure for railway noise.

- The single event level, SEL

SEL is a measure similar in concept to L_{Aeq} but is used to describe the noise from an individual train. The time period over which SEL is based is a standard one second. SEL has two main applications:

(i)   for direct comparisons of individual noise events, such as between two trains or between a train and a bus; and
(ii) as a means of calculating L_{Aeq} from a knowledge of the number of train pass-bys and the corresponding time period. Individual SEL values are added logarithmically and averaged over the exposed time period.

Vibration: In the theory of physics, there is no clear distinction between sound and vibration. Sound is a vibratory phenomenon, although vibration generally refers to the motion of solid objects. Transmission of vibration through solid objects is often referred to as structure-borne, whereas transmission through the ground is referred to as ground-borne.

In contrast to sound, vibration is often specified in terms of absolute magnitudes of displacement, velocity, or acceleration. However, vibration levels are also commonly used and recommended since they are standardised measurements and facilitate the task of comparing results. Standard reference quantities for vibration levels are shown in Table 19.1. These should be clearly stated when vibration levels are presented. Unlike sound levels, there are no generally accepted weighting curves that can be used to evaluate human perception of vibration levels.

Vibration Levels	Definition	Commonly Used Reference Quantity
Acceleration	$L_a = 20\log_{10}(a/a_o)$	$a_o = 10^{-5}$ m/s^2
Velocity	$L_v = 20\log_{10}(v/v_o)$	$v_o = 10^{-8}$ m/s
Displacement	$L_d = 20\log_{10}(d/d_o)$	$d_o = 10^{-11}$ m

Table 19.1 Standard Vibration Reference Quantities.

The Importance of Controlling Noise and Vibration

Compared to other sources of transport noise (such as road traffic and aircraft) railway noise is generally accepted, and studies confirm it as less annoying at similar noise levels. Nevertheless, to many wayside communities, railway noise may be the dominant noise source and a significant cause of annoyance. However, noise and vibration from rail operations can be more than just annoying. They can startle people and interfere with a whole range of activities including conversation, sleep, listening to the radio or television, periods of relaxation, reading and so on[2]. Permanent damage to hearing is most unlikely among the wayside community but high noise and vibration levels from trains can cause anxiety, fear and stress. For staff working on the system they can cause much more severe impacts such as deafness and even death, if operating noise blots out the sound from warning devices. Excessive running noise diminishes the attractiveness of a rail system as an alternative mode of transport to the private car, can be the cause of adverse economic and environmental impacts (such as a reduction in property values in areas subject to high noise levels), and can create anti-rail lobbies against future rail developments.

Sources of Railway Noise and Vibration

Noise from a rail system can reach the community from various sources, each emanating from different operations that make up the system. These include train operation, track maintenance, yard operations and activities, ventilation shafts, substation transformers and cooling fans, and station heating, ventilation and air conditioning systems. The ensuing discussion is restricted mainly to noise and vibration from train operations which affect the majority of exposed communities. The most widespread and common source of noise is that which is generated by the interaction between the steel wheel and steel rail while the vehicle is in motion.

Wheel/Rail Interaction: Wheel/rail interaction results in a noise that is generally divided into three distinct categories: squeal, impact and roar.

Squeal is the term used to describe the intense high-frequency noise, consisting of one or more tones, heard when rail cars go round curves of small radius[5]. For example, so severe were BR's problems with wheel squeal with non-bogie rolling stock on some of their Cornish branch lines that they have had to design special rolling stock (the Class 153). Several factors can cause wheel squeal, three of which have been identified for the purpose of squeal noise control:

(i)   differential slip between inner and outer wheels on a solid axle which occurs on a sharp curve, where the outer wheel has to cover more distance than the inner wheel; this differential velocity is compensated by one or both of the wheels slipping on the rails;

(ii) rubbing of wheel flanges against the rail; and

(iii) lateral creep (crabbing) of the wheels across the rail head. As the rail car rounds the curve, its wheels cannot run at a tangent to the rails because they are constrained by the carriage's rigidity. Hence, as the wheels roll along the rail, they must also creep laterally across the rail head in order to follow the curve, since the rigid axles are forced to remain parallel.

Studies on the influence of the ratio of curve radius to bogie wheelbase on the occurrence of squeal have been carried out on the Massachusetts Bay Transportation Authority (MBTA) system in Boston, USA. The results showed that for curves with a ratio of curve radius to bogie wheelbase of 50 or less, squeal was virtually guaranteed, whereas if the ratio exceeded 200, it was very unlikely.

Impact noise is generated by discontinuities on the running surfaces of wheels and rails. Flat spots on wheels (caused by braking), rail joints and special trackwork are all responsible for impact noise. The familiar "clickety-clack" associated with trains that run on tracks with jointed rails is an example of impact noise.

Roar noise is the wheel/rail noise that predominates on a straight track in the absence of discontinuities on the wheel and rail running surface, such as wheel-flats and rail-joints respectively. Roar noise is attributed to the micro-scale roughness (corrugations) on the running surfaces of the wheel and the rail, exciting both into vibration. In turn, this vibration is radiated as wheel/rail noise to the surrounding area.

Sources of Vibration: Vibration is generated by the interaction of steel wheels rolling on steel rails, and is influenced by a number of factors which include the surface conditions of wheels and rails, train speed, track suspension, rail support structure and type of wheels. The vibration generated by the wheel/rail interaction is transmitted through the rail fasteners to the track structure, where it propagates through the soil to the foundations of adjacent buildings. The resulting vibration of the building may be perceptible, either as a mechanical motion (such as floor shaking) or/and as an audible low frequency rumble which sometimes causes windows and crockery to rattle. Perceptible vibration usually occurs at the low frequency range of 10 to 30 Hz.

Planning for Noise and Vibration

New Rail Systems: There are several phases in the planning process, from the initial conception of the scheme to its operation, where noise and vibration impacts are considered. At the initial stage of planning, when a rail system is one of the options being considered, the fact that a rail system will generate less noise and other forms of pollution than a new road handling a similar passenger volume is a factor in its favour.

During the option evaluation phase, an environmental impact analysis of all competing systems should be included. Vehicle type and technology are usually selected during this phase. Other items that deserve consideration are:

- land use along the proposed route. Noise will provoke less protest in an area of industrial activity than in a peaceful residential area;
- station locations. These should be located so as to be accessible both by car and bus (and on foot), but not too close to residential areas where station and traffic activities can be a nuisance to residents;
- alignment. Making maximum use of existing rail tracks and highway medians can reduce noise impact, while the former will minimise the need for compulsory purchase of land and property;
- underground construction type (for example, deep tunnel vs cut-and cover).

The next phase after the preliminary option evaluation is the preliminary engineering and design phase. During this phase, a final environmental impact statement may be prepared, including a detailed analysis of the noise and vibration impact along the proposed railway corridor. The analysis may be based on empirical data from a similar system elsewhere or on a mathematical method of estimating noise exposure under the different conditions that exist. The following should also be considered:

- the specification for vehicle noise and vibration performance, as well as reduction features such as vehicle skirts, resilient wheels and type of suspension;
- locations where abatement measures (such sound barriers or rubber pads under the rails) will be required;
- conceptual designs of specific abatement measures with prototypes being designed and, if possible, tested;
- the designs of aerial structures should be evaluated to ensure that structure-radiated noise will not be a problem;
- location conditions that may enhance the propagation of noise or vibration (for example ground conditions) must be investigated, especially, for the latter, where an underground section is planned.

Several detailed aspects of noise and vibration must be considered during the final stage, including:

- the final alignment. Efforts should be made to provide a buffer zone of 50 to 100m, wherever possible, to minimise acoustical impacts; potential problem sections should be identified;
- specifications for noise and vibration control designs (such as of materials for acoustical absorption treatment, and of resilient pads for floating slabs and their installation);
- acoustical analysis of section design, and where previously determined noise or vibration criteria will be exceeded, the relevant control procedures;
- track maintenance. This is often overlooked and can create serious community resentment. Procedures that minimise its effects on the community should be developed.

During construction, effort should be made to monitor compliance with, for example, the general recommendations set out in BS5228: Parts 1-4: 1984-1986; "Noise Control on Construction and Open Sites". Normally, construction contracts include specifications of maximum noise; this may require the help of a noise specialist to monitor the noise levels.

Acoustical tests should be performed as soon as operational testing of trains and of other facilities begin. These are usually carried out on the completion of a section of the system, and they are useful for:

1) evaluating of how well the system is performing with respect to specifications;
2) investigating of problems not anticipated;
3) reviewing previous designs and their environmental impact; and
4) providing information for use in future designs.

In cases where problems identified cannot be put right, the testing exercise will provide the operating authority time to devise strategies for handling complaints before they occur on a large scale.

At the start of commercial operation, procedures for evaluating complaints, and a monitoring system for noise and vibration, should be devised. The knowledge gained should enable the operator to draw up schedules for the maintenance of the system in order to avoid excessive noise and vibration from wheel flats or rail corrugations; items to be covered include wheel truing and rail grinding.

Existing Systems: In the case of an existing rail system, the operating authority is generally aware of noise and vibration problems and the impact these have on the community. In serious cases, the latter is usually translated into recorded complaints to the authority or/and to local newspapers.

Mitigation measures can, however, be prohibitively expensive. In addition to the regular maintenance of rails and wheels, other measures that can be implemented include:

- the use of welded rail to replace jointed track;
- the use of absorption material to reduce reflected sound from underground, off retaining walls or sound barrier surfaces;
- the use of sound barriers along surface or aerial track sections to reduce wayside noise;
- the use of resilient vibration isolation components when underground (and sometimes also surface) track works are upgraded;
- the inclusion of noise and vibration emission specifications when purchasing new vehicles;
- the use of resilient wheels to replace solid steel wheels in order to reduce wheel squeal noise and vibration levels;
- the use of vibration isolation or damping treatments on steel aerial structures to reduce structure-radiated noise.

In extreme cases, consideration might be given to reducing train speed along sensitive sections of a route.

Tyne and Wear Metro - A Case-Study

Background: Tyne and Wear Metro was the first passenger railway system of its kind in the UK. It is a modern overhead electric rapid transit system which replaced an old diesel multiple unit (DMU) train system. The system, operated by the Tyne and Wear Passenger Transport Executive (TWPTE), was enhanced by a transport policy which integrated train and bus services in the form of several interchanges with ample free car parking facilities.

The Study: The study[8] was conducted by the author in 1983, on a section of a route opened nearly a year earlier. DMU operations had ceased in 1980 to allow for construction and other related activities.

The objectives of the study included, among others:

- a comprehensive noise measurement survey of the study area;
- an assessment of the wayside community reactions to Metro noise;
- determining the noise indices best related to annoyance caused by Metro noise;
- assessing how serious Metro-caused vibration was; and
- suggesting means of alleviating noise-related problems.

The Findings: The main findings of the study were:

- the Metro was surprisingly noisy. Peak levels of over 90dBA were recorded at facades 15 metres away from the tracks, while the corresponding exposure levels were over $70L_{eq,18hr}$.

An earlier study commissioned by TWPTE concluded that noise levels from the Metro were comparable to those from DMU's, and that the greater frequency of services would make the noise exposure, over a whole day, from the Metro greater than that experienced from DMU's.

- residents' perception of noise from the Metro was generally more favourable than their perception of noise from DMU trains.

This should be viewed with the efficient and high profile image of the Metro against an ageing, less efficient and slower DMU service.

- L_{Aeq} was shown to be as good, if not the most practical, noise index for measuring railway noise annoyance, when compared to other

212

indices which combined noise levels and frequency and which applied a different weighting to evening time noise levels respectively.

An 18 hour exposure period (ie. $L_{Aeq,18hr}$) was used to reflect the duration of operations of the Metro.

- Over 50 percent of residents living along the tracks experienced vibration from the Metro. A number of them believed that the vibration was or could be the cause of some from of structural damage to their property. It was claimed, however, by those who lived in the area when the DMU's were in operation, that vibration from the Metro was less.
- as an existing system, the following first steps were recommended on the basis of responses obtained from residents during the study:
  - to plan and carry out a regular maintenance programme of the rolling stock and trackworks. The programme would require a set of criteria specifying for example, the minimum length and number of wheel-flats, the maximum roughness of rails and wheels in order to plan when wheel and/or rail grinding should occur.
  - to inform residents ahead of night-time maintenance operations, as noise from tamping and track aligning machines were often described by residents as their worst noise experience.

The Legal Standpoint

Unlike the advice on the procedures for the measurement of road traffic noise[1], there are no similar national guidelines or standards for the measurement of noise from railways as yet. However, in the few cases where new railways have been opened in recent years, noise insulation criteria have been set and implemented by railway operators. Table 19.2 summarises the noise criteria that have been applied in these cases.

Authority/Operator	Railway	Noise Insulation Criterion (facade level L_{Aeq})	
Tower Hamlets/ Docklands Light Railway	Docklands Light Railway (Beckton Extension)	65	24 hour
South Tyneside/ Tyne and Wear PTE	Tyneside Metro	60	24 hour
Selby District Council/ British Rail	East Coast Main Line Diversion	(1)	
Greater London Council/ British Rail	Liverpool Street Redevelopment	(1)	

Table 19.2. Noise Insulation Criteria for New Railways in Britain
(1) No limits given but insulation offered to adversely affected property.

A recent British Government report[4] includes a number of recommendations for Britain's first national rail noise protection standard. The recommendations, which will be applied to all new railway lines (except for railways running underground and Light Rapid Transit systems running on roads) were based on achieving parity with the protection provided for people living near new roads. They took into account the differences that exist both in the character of the noise generated by roads and railways and in the way the two forms of transport are operated. The recommendations include, among others, the following:

- the noise level near the track should be determined using the A-weighted scale and expressed in terms of the equivalent noise level L_{Aeq} averaged over a specified time period;
- those responsible for a new railway should have a duty to offer to insulate against noise those rooms of dwellings near the new railway line that are exposed to a facade noise level from the railway of:

(1) at least 66 dBA L_{Aeq}, 24 hr, and/or
(2) at least 61 dBA L_{Aeq}, night (2300 to 0700);

- the noise level should be those expected under the noisiest operating conditions anticipated in the 15 years after the opening of the new line.

The report also recommends that the Secretary of State should consider including a maximum noise level (L_{Amax}) in the standard for insulating dwelling against noise from new railways.

References

1. Department of Transport and Welsh Office (1988) "Calculation of Road Traffic Noise", HMSO.
2. Hann Tucker (1990) Evidence to the Select Committee on the British Railways (No. 3) Bill (HL). House of Lords, London, June.
3. Hassall, J.R. & Zaveri, K. (1979) "Acoustic Noise Measurements", Bruel & Kjaer, Denmark.
4. "Railway Noise and The Insulation of Dwellings" (1991) ("the Mitchell Report"). Report of the Committee formed to recommend to the Secretary of State for Transport a national noise insulation standard for new railway lines, The Department of Transport, HMSO, London.
5. Rudd M. J. (1976) "Wheel/Rail Noise II: Wheel Squeal", *Jnl. of Sound and Vibration Ctrl.* 46(3) pp. 381-394.

6. Saurenman, H.J. Nelson, J.T. & Wilson, G.P. (1982) "Handbook of Urban Rail Noise and Vibration Control", UMTA-MA-06-0049-82-1, U.S. Department of Transportation, Washington.
7. Rupert Taylor and Partners Ltd (1981) "Tyne and Wear Metro : Study of Noise and Vibration Levels affecting dwellings bordering the Haymarket - Tynemouth Section", Acoustic Report, London.
8. Thancanamootoo, S. (1987) "Impact of Noise from Urban Railway Operations", PhD Thesis, University of Newcastle upon Tyne, U.K.

20. Involving Property Developers

Michael Schabas

Introduction: Funding Urban Railway Developments

There is no shortage of urban passenger railway schemes. Virtually every city has aspirations to build one, and most cities of a million inhabitants or more get one sooner or later. Wanting, however, is not enough to ensure that one will receive. Urban railways are expensive, and somebody needs to be convinced to pay for them. The challenge of the urban rail planner is to conceive, design, and promote a scheme that people will be convinced to pay for, either directly or indirectly.

Willingness to pay is the best test of a project's value. If people will pay for something freely, then it is probably worthwhile. Moreover if a project is financially profitable one can simply go to a bank and borrow the money. However, few urban railway schemes are profitable; most only cover a fraction of total costs from passenger fares. Projects that do get built usually depend on a significant government subsidy, which is often justified by prospective benefits in terms of reduced air pollution and traffic congestion.

The remaining benefits of urban rail systems are usually described in terms of "improving the efficiency of a city". Nobody pays directly for this, but if it really happens it should ultimately be reflected in property values. Property owners and developers, who are widely believed to capture windfall gains when new rail lines are built, are thus a third target for funding. In fact the potential for financing new rail lines with increased property values is often overstated, first because the timing of benefits will not match the timing of expenditures, and secondly because special and controversial mechanisms including taxes and negotiated "contributions" are required if the benefit is to be captured.

If rail promoters genuinely seek to recover system costs from property developers, they need to understand exactly how a rail line will benefit a property. This depends very much on the type of development that may be possible, with and without the rail line. They may also need to make significant changes to the project itself, in terms of design and implementation. This may not be a bad thing, as a the success or failure of a rail line may be measured at least partly in its effects on urban development. A rail scheme that generates dramatic benefits in terms of property development is very likely a worthwhile scheme in other ways, while a scheme that has no impact on property may also attract few passengers and have little benefit at all.

Property Development and Planning Permission

Before the advent of mechanised transport, people could not commute more than a mile or two and land values dropped sharply outside of city centres. At the turn of the century railway and tram builders often bought land on the fringes of major cities, whether New York, London, or Tokyo, and developed it profitably as suburban housing. In a few cases railway builders insisted on cash contributions from property owners before they would stop commuter trains at local stations.

But this is no longer the case. With the advent of widespread car ownership government has long accepted an implicit obligation to provide a comprehensive road network. Improved rail services may allow higher density development, and may change the focus of a suburb from road to rail orientation, but it is unlikely to determine whether development of any sort is viable. Even London, with a limited road network, has some suburbs without any rail service and yet which are quite prosperous nonetheless.

Nowadays, planning permission is far more important to the feasibility of development than transport facilities; however, permission can be explicitly linked with provision of a rail service. There may be nothing wrong in principle with this type of linkage, but planners extracting payments from a developer to fund rail improvements should not pretend that these are necessarily related to a real increase in value.

Commercial Development

When a rail line is built into a commercial area, there are three types of possible benefit to commercial property. First, there is a general increase in accessibility. If existing transport corridors are saturated, the rail line may allow further growth both in the concentration of employment and in property values. This can, of course, only happen if there is underlying economic demand for more development.

A recent example of this type of benefit is in Los Angeles, where a new and very expensive underground Metro system is under construction. The project was delayed for years as the City, State, and Federal governments debated who should pay and whether it was indeed worthwhile at all. Finally, a collection of downtown business interests actually voted to impose a tax on all commercial space within one-half mile of the new Metro stations, to finance system construction. The tax will raise about 10% of the total capital cost, and the line will need operating subsidies as well, but this unusual gesture was sufficient to get action and funding from Government.

Note that in Los Angeles the tax is levied on all commercial space within a one-half mile radius even though all studies show that most people will only walk half this distance from the station to their office. The half-mile radius is nonetheless reasonable because office workers within this area still compete for road space when commuting. Also the Los Angeles tax only applies in the downtown area, where roads are now saturated throughout the day. Although the rail line also serves commercial areas outside the city centre, growth of these areas is not considered to be constrained by transport capacity, as such, and so no offer to make a contribution was forthcoming. Property owners outside the city centre were not so desperate to have the Metro built, and did not make an offer to tax themselves. They will be served by the Metro as "free riders", in economists' jargon.

A second type of benefit to commercial property can be realised by specific land uses such as high turnover retail. Shopping centre developers in Toronto, Washington, and London have paid substantial sums towards improved connections into railway stations, in some cases simply to redirect existing pedestrian traffic to pass shop frontages. Banks have paid for the right to install their cash dispensers adjacent to ticket machines, and in one city they are in fact the same machines. Elsewhere, however, stations and ancillary facilities have been designed in such a way as virtually to preclude associated commercial development. Large bus loops, vast machine rooms, and badly arranged entrance corridors can preclude the provision of retail spaces which could have been an important convenience to passengers as well as a useful source of revenue.

Third, independent of any need for increased capacity, a new high-speed rail line may enlarge the effective catchment area for a commercial centre. Retail centres compete for spatial dominance, while office centres compete based on their employee catchment areas. With good rail connections, suburban shopping centres may compete aggressively for business with traditional downtown stores. Examples are Yorkdale Shopping Centre in Toronto (which is linked into the Spadina Subway) and Kingston-upon-Thames outside London which actually pays British Rail to operate extra trains to bring shoppers from inner London.

Centres such as Croydon (south of London) and Newark (west of New York City) promote themselves as secondary office locations, with lower rents but good rail connections back into and across the primary city centres. To succeed in attracting office tenants out of established centres without extreme disruption they need to be able to draw on the same commuter catchment as the established centres, so that existing employees do not all need to "up sticks" and move house. Of course over time many employees of relocating companies will move their homes closer to the new office, but the extent to which this can be minimised will increase the attractiveness of the new location.

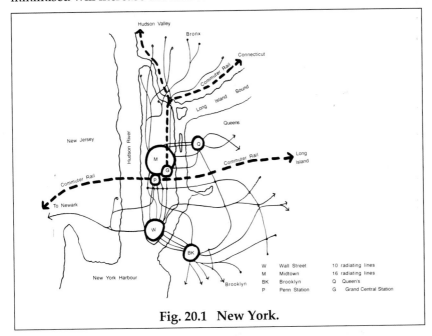

Fig. 20.1 New York.

Most of the Manhattan "subway" lines run north-south, crossing over to Brooklyn in the south and Queens and the Bronx in the north. Although the historic business centre is around Wall Street at the tip of Manhattan, the main commuter rail terminals are two miles north and only half a mile south of the new "Midtown" district. Rockefeller Center, built in the 1930s and 1960s, is the established heart of Midtown Manhattan which altogether now accommodates more than 150,000 workers.

Newark, a smaller and historically less fashionable address, is linked directly to both Wall Street and Midtown by subway lines, and is also at a junction of many commuter lines from the western New Jersey suburbs. It has thus been recently developed as a centre in its own right, with some major companies moving their headquarters and "back offices" to take advantage of lower rents.

219

Where a new office centre aspires to compete on equal terms with the old downtown, as at Rockefeller Centre in New York, La Defense in Paris, Shinjuku in Tokyo or Canary Wharf in London, rail commuter connections need to be very good, with trip times roughly equal for a similarly large employee catchment area (see Figures 20.1-20.3). Rockefeller Centre in midtown Manhattan was built within a short walk

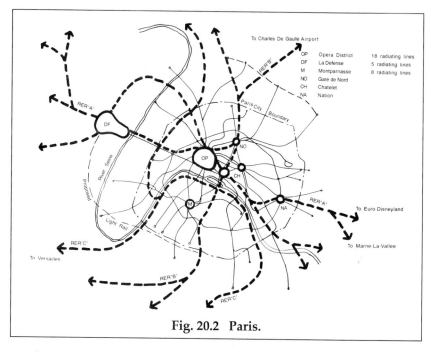

Fig. 20.2   Paris.

Until the 1960s Paris had no integrated regional rail system. Intercity rail lines ended at terminals along the edge of the 19th century walled city. The Metro served internal circulation trips but did not extend beyond the old walls. Interchange between the Metro and mainline railways was poor. The premier business centre was in the Opera area, served by the Metro and by the most intensive commuter rail terminal, the Gare St Lazare with lines in from the affluent western suburbs.

Construction of the RER cross-Paris rail lines allowed development of intensive commuter services from the north, south, and east, with direct trains or a single transfer to new business centres which have been developed in a ring around the Paris region. The largest new business centre is La Defense, built 1960 - 1990 with about 100,000 employees and the headquarters of many of France's largest companies.

of two existing subway lines and the Grand Central commuter terminal, but only with construction of the Sixth Avenue Subway in the late 1930s did it become easily accessible from the vast suburbs in Long Island and New Jersey. La Defense was built astride the main commuter rail lines from the west, but the massive RER Express Metro was required to provide comparable high speed connections from the dormitory suburbs of eastern Paris.

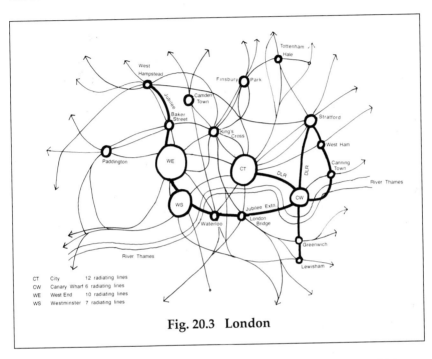

Fig. 20.3 London

London has two historic centres, the City and the West End. As in Tokyo a "circle" line links them and most of the suburban rail terminals together, and early in this century "tube" lines were built which short-cut across the circle. Many of the suburban lines also run directly to both the City and West End.

The third centre, now being developed around Canary Wharf in London Docklands, already has a direct connection back to the City, and a link via Stratford to most of the commuter rail lines from the northeast. Construction of the Jubilee Line Extension will give a fast connection back to the West End and intercept most of the remaining commuter rail services from the south and west. By the end of the decade it is expected that there will be more than 100,000 people working in and around Canary Wharf.

Perhaps the most spectacular and recent example of rail line construction affecting property development is in London Docklands. Since construction began on the Docklands Light Railway (DLR), an area of mostly derelict docks has seen massive redevelopment as high density, high quality offices (see also Chapter 14). After the initial DLR was completed, the Canary Wharf developers offered a substantial financial contribution to increase capacity and build an extension into the old City of London. In fact, they offered to pay half the cost of these works, with the rest being financed by government on the basis of traffic congestion benefits and anticipated increased profits (or rather decreased losses) on the London rail system as a whole. The DLR upgrading gave the necessary capacity, while the City extension provides the necessary strategic link to allow Canary Wharf to function as a modern annex to the old City. The station at Canary Wharf has been rebuilt entirely at the developer's expense as an integral part of a shopping complex, with access directly off the platforms. This is extremely convenient for passengers, and should also be profitable in its own right.

By the end of 1992, with the Bank extension and upgrading, the DLR will provide ample capacity for the projected development of Canary Wharf through to the end of the century. However, DLR only provides good access from the City, northeast London and certain specific corridors in north and west London with good interchange at Bank. Existing companies in the "old" centre of London are reluctant to move to Canary Wharf if it means that many staff will face much longer trip times, or that they must move house. Moreover, other developments adjacent to Canary Wharf are underway which could overload the DLR.

The Canary Wharf developer thus offered a £400 million contribution towards the construction of a second rail line, this time an extension of the Jubilee line to the City and West End and intercepting commuter rail lines from the south and west. No doubt over time many new Canary Wharf employees will relocate their homes from west to east London, but with construction of the Jubilee line this is no longer so necessary as travel times from the south western suburbs to Canary Wharf will be almost identical to travel times to other parts of the Central area.

High Density Residential Development

In the 1960s and 1970s several cities successfully encouraged high density residential development around suburban rail stations; the two pre-eminent examples are Toronto and Stockholm.

Beginning in the 1950s the Stockholm city government built several new towns on large vacant sites which had been purchased before the second World War and "land banked". Vallingby and Farsta, with medium and high density apartments clustered around the Metro station with pedestrianised community centres were widely admired and copied by British new town planners.

Toronto followed a somewhat different model. The subway has followed rather than led suburban development; however it has been City policy to encourage private redevelopment of suitable areas around stations (see Figure 20.4). Depending upon the character of the surrounding community this has resulted in everything ranging from comprehensive mixed commercial and residential redevelopment (as at Sheppard, Eglinton and St Clair), high-density residential with only a small commercial element (High Park, Davisville), or in some cases protection of existing stable communities against any change.

The main instruments used have been official plan designation of an area, followed by granting of planning permission to private developers who have assembled suitable redevelopment sites on the open market. The city complements planning designation with construction of

Fig. 20.4 Photo of Toronto

Looking along the route of the Toronto Subway the underground stations can be easily identified by the clusters of commercial and residential development which has been encouraged, while protecting the surrounding stable residential neighbourhoods.

223

adequate infrastructure such as trunk sewers and water mains to support the uses set out in the official plan.

One can admire the success of the Toronto and Stockholm planning efforts, and unlike some other city building efforts of the 1960s these high density communities have, by and large, aged gracefully. However as paradigms for urban railway builders at the end of the 20th century they are probably of limited value. Most modern cities now have too much multi-family housing. Also it is much more difficult to assemble large sites on the open market, at least in residential areas. Community groups are more sophisticated and would not now tolerate some of the property assembly tactics used to dislodge "holdouts".

Suburban Residential Development

Beckton Park and Port Greenwich are two recent housing developments by British Gas plc in London (see Figure 14.3). Both are being built on former gas works adjacent to the River Thames. Both are being served by new rail lines to Central London.

Beckton Park, approximately 5 miles east of Central London, has been developed during the 1980s as a medium density residential area, mostly with clustered and linked terrace homes. There are already good road connections outwards to the suburban motorway system, but until 1993 the fastest link to central London is by express bus. With some 5,000 homes already sold and occupied, less than 500 passengers regularly ride the express bus each morning. It seems that commuting into Central London is unimportant to the residents of Beckton Park, presumably because there are plenty of other jobs in the area accessible by private car. Of course, once the Beckton rail link opens the area may become more attractive to central London workers, but it is unclear when or how this will be reflected in property values.

Beckton will be served by a rail extension funded almost entirely by government subsidy. The line was first proposed in 1981 and was finally approved for construction in 1989. With completion in 1993 it will have been a full decade from conception to completion, and so if the overall effect is to raise property values by, say, 20% this would be reflected in an average increase of less than 2% per year, barely discernable as property prices can fluctuate by 10% to 20% in one year. Although there was an attempt to recover some of the cost from property value increases, this has been abandoned as property values seem to have actually fallen since construction began on the line.

Port Greenwich is, as the crow flies, much closer to Central London and actually just across the river from Canary Wharf. Development there has proceeded more slowly because the local planning authority has been less favourable, and the site is badly contaminated. However the main reason claimed for the delay is poor transport links. In fact the site is bisected by the Blackwall Tunnel, a high capacity route extending South to Dover and North to Docklands and the City. One can drive from Port Greenwich to Central London in 45 minutes, even in the morning peak hour. So the site is hardly inaccessible.

The truth is that, without other transport improvements, development of Port Greenwich would further overload existing road links precisely because the site is so accessible. This would be at the expense of existing commuters from suburbs further out. Currently in the morning peak there can be a two mile queue to enter the Blackwall Tunnel from the south. Port Greenwich residents would be in a position to join at the front of the queue.

For the Port Greenwich scheme, the Department of Transport and the local planning authority have insisted that British Gas make a substantial contribution towards the cost of an extension to the Jubilee Underground line, virtually as a precondition of planning permission. The Department of Transport, which is paying the bulk of the cost of the Jubilee line, actually threatened to route the line via Blackwall, thereby missing Port Greenwich, unless a contribution was forthcoming (see Figure 14.3). Whether this is good public policy, or fair and equitable is another matter.

Homeowners in Beckton Park are getting their rail line for free, while Port Greenwich will be paying £25 million. Of course this may be effectively paid out of reduced profits to British Gas, but given the cost of decontaminating the soil and building other necessary infrastructure such as roads, the result could well be to delay construction of the housing entirely. This, of course, will benefit nobody.

Involving Developers Early

It has already been noted how some systems, particularly new heavy rail systems in sprawling American cities, have actually been designed and built in a manner which discourages close integration with other urban development. A rail transit system is an artery of the City, but it can only function to its full potential if it is closely knitted into the city fabric.

Where a new rail line is being constructed within an already densely built-up part of the city, the sheer economics of property purchase will force designers to minimize land take and to provide entrances and structures of an appropriate scale. However when a new rail lines is built through undeveloped or under-developed land, particular care must be taken to ensure that the facilities are built in a manner which will encourage the development of complementary uses. This can be best done in a "strong" property market by working directly with a specific developer, either one who already controls adjacent property or by entering directly into some sort of joint venture arrangement. British Rail has successfully applied the joint venture approach in the redevelopment of several central London rail terminals (e.g. Charing Cross), while Vancouver has negotiated transit corridors across development sites owned by others.

Where there is no immediate prospect of development, the transit system designer can best ensure compatibility with future development prospects by retaining an architect and planning consultant to develop hypothetical schemes, to determine the appropriate protection for integration with the railway. This approach has been used on many urban railway schemes particularly in the USA, but it is highly speculative and there is no guarantee that development will actually happen in the way anticipated.

The Potential for Developer Contributions
Clearly there can be a strong inter-relationship between urban rail construction and development, but how this is manifested in developer interest or contributions depends very much on specific circumstances both of the route, design, land ownership, and timing. Developers are in business to make money, and in most cities there are plenty of sites awaiting development which already have good transport available. Beckton Park was a viable housing site even without the rail line, although the prospect of the railway being built some day in the future may have added a slight fillip to sales. Rockefeller Centre did not begin construction until the Sixth Avenue subway was itself solidly committed and under construction. La Defense was a government-coordinated project which took more than three decades to fruition, with private investment only cautiously following government funding of road and rail construction; even today it is still incomplete.

In Toronto, Washington, and Hong Kong urban railway projects have recovered a significant share of capital costs from the sale and redevelopment of surplus lands and "air rights" over stations and depots. However the net profits, after allowing for carrying charges and costs, rarely recover more than the costs of property acquisition for the line as a whole.

Only in exceptional circumstances will a developer link its fortunes to a project which may have a time span of ten years or more from conception, through construction to commissioning (plus a large measure of uncertainty, at least at the beginning). Ten years is simply too long to interest property developers paying interest rates of 10% per year or more. In the specific circumstances of Canary Wharf, the rail project itself was quite small and could be built quickly while the development was massive and would necessarily take several years. So rail and property were, exceptionally, on a similar programme. Moreover the strength of the London property market, and release from onerous planning controls, created an exceptional opportunity.

If rail planners want to repeat the example of Canary Wharf, they need to shape their schemes specifically to do so. The routes need to be selected not only to relieve existing traffic flows, whether on streets or other railways, but also to open up strategic linkages to specific development sites. For Canary Wharf, it was essential that the Jubilee Extension linked into the West End and to the south London commuter rail lines. Other routes were studied which would have attracted similar traffic volumes but would not have offered the same strategic linkage; Canary Wharf would have become a "back office" district, without the ability to grow into a metropolitan centre on a par with the City and West End.

Schemes need to be designed to be implemented quickly. This does not imply careless haste either in construction or environmental impacts; indeed, quite the reverse. In a modern city one can only build a rail line if impacts on other properties are mitigated or compensated acceptably. The Jubilee line extension was deliberately routed through less-developed parts of South London, mostly in deep tunnel under an existing rail line, to minimize the likelihood of community opposition which would cause delays. Most construction work is actually being done from riverside sites so barges can be used rather than road haulage.

Cash Up Front or Taxes?

Ultimately, the only purpose of an urban passenger railway is to make the city function more efficiently. Developer contributions, where they arise, are a good market signal that a scheme is worthwhile, but there is a vast gap between this and suggesting that lines should be wholly or substantially funded by property development. Certainly the absence of any developer interest in a rail scheme should cast doubts upon its merits, but the absence of any cash contributions cannot in any way be taken as conclusive evidence that the scheme is not a worthwhile public investment.

Nor should the dispersion of benefits among a great many properties, all of whom will do their best to be "free riders", be seen negatively. If there are benefits, these will eventually be recaptured at least in part through taxes, both from property and from incomes resulting from the general increase in urban efficiency. Pursuit of private developer contributions can be a valuable and potentially rewarding part of any urban rail scheme; however, it should not become an obsession.

References

Schabas, M. (1988) "Quantitative Analysis of Rapid Transit Alignment Alternatives", *Transpn. Quat.* 42 pp. 403-416.

Schabas, M (1990) "Planning and Developing Light Rail - the Developer's Role", Symposium on Potential of Light Transit Systems in British Cities, Nottingham (March).

21. The Railway Investment Process

Ernest Godward

Introduction
Appraisal of rail projects and operations tends to come at the end of the planning process whereas it really should come close to the start and continue throughout the project. It is no use starting to plan a project without knowing (at least indicatively) what benefits will arise. Before the railways were nationalised, financial appraisals of projects were carried out e.g. of the London and North Eastern Railways electrification scheme in 1931[15], where the appraisal was a simple financial assessment of replacing steam with electric traction. Now railways tend to be nationalised industries, appraisals may also take into account the wider social benefits arising from railways compared with other modes of transport.

The Appraisal Process
The appraisal process consists of six main elements:-
a). Project generation;
b). Estimation of cash flows;
c). Internal refinement process;
d). Analysis and selection of projects;
e). Authorisation of expenditure and
f). Post Implementation Review.

Project Generation
Many ideas for projects start with the statement "Wouldn't it be a good idea if . . . ?". Some organisations, including railways, have used more formal idea-generating techniques to throw up projects worthy of consideration; for example, London Underground Limited used "brain storming" sessions to develop ideas for the modernisation of the company's Northern Line.

However, railway managers must remember that they do not have a monopoly of good ideas, which may come at any time from anywhere in the organisation or, indeed, from outside. Perhaps the sign of a good railway management is that it is able to listen, take on board ideas and develop them quickly to a successful conclusion. Stewart & Chadwick[16] quote an example in their book involving a passenger, one of the authors and Chris Green, then general manager of the BR Scotrail sector, on a night sleeper train from Edinburgh to London.

Having established that an idea might prove useful the rail planner needs to assess (usually on the back of an envelope or cigarette packet[8]) the viability of the proposal. Costs and benefits are assessed over the life of the project and discounted back to the base year. Provided that benefits are greater than costs in NPV terms (see below) then the project should be included in the plans for further development.

The reason for discounting is that money has a time value. Money invested will give interest over time, e.g. £100 invested now would be worth £108 in a years time if the interest rate were 8% per annum. Individuals and firms prefer the money now so they can consume goods and services. It is little consolation to a railway company if its political masters decide that a capital grant will be given next year if they need to purchase new rolling stock this year. This problem becomes more apparent when one considers that inflation is present in all modern economies. For example goods costing £100 this year will cost £105 next year if the inflation rate is 5% p.a.. Risk, too, is also very important. Having the money now could minimise the risks. The Net Present Value (NPV) is therefore the sum of future cash flows discounted back to the start date of the project.

The Planning Horizon

Generally speaking most railways have a series of plans. The plans range from the strategic long term plans (with horizons from 20 years up to 100 years) down to short term plans for next year (usually incorporating the budget). There are those who criticise such long term plans but techniques such as scenario planning can give options as to which routes railways might take towards their future. A decision to buy rolling stock in effect freezes the organisation into a particular technology or design for 30 to 40 years.

The long gestation period that is common with larger railway projects in the UK needs to be incorporated into the sensitivity testing within the investment process. The problem is that delays of up to 25 years (particularly in the case of planning of London Railways) do not make for meaningful sensitivity testing. Perhaps a maximum delay of up to five years is the most sensible, after which the project assumptions need to be revisited.

Studies of two schemes in the West Midlands[8,9] show delays of up to four years between "proof" and implementation. The delays were not only due to Government delays but delays caused by the need to interface with other projects such as Light Rapid Transit, general planning of urban environments and financing limitations. The MMC study of LUL showed a delay of over 25 years between first inception of the Chelsea - Hackney line in 1974[2] to possible completion and operation in the early part of the next century. The Central London Rail Study[4] showed the line had a benefit to cost ratio of 0.9:1, but taken with the East West Crossrail scheme the ratio was 1.1:1. East West Crossrail was given Ministerial approval in 1990.

Estimation of Cash Flows

The estimation of cash flows and the assessment thereof is essentially a mechanical process. In the past reference to a set of tables was the norm. Today, the appraisal of cash flows is considerably assisted by computer- or spreadsheet-type programs with functions that produce NPVs at the push of a key.

A typical analysis for an imaginary new rail route is shown below in Table 21.1. The flows are discounted at 8%, which has been the accepted rate for both BR and LUL since 1990. The 8% discount rate represents the opportunity cost of capital to the nationalised railway operators in the UK but actually reflects the stakeholders' opportunity cost; the stakeholder in the UK is the Government.

Inputs into the Cashflow Estimation Process

An understanding of the costs and benefits arising from projects are needed, as are the underlying processes that determine travel habits. Chapter 17 has discussed costs, whilst chapters 3 and 9 go some way to explaining in econometric and mathematical terms the processes that determine travel habits. The translation of travel times into monetary values has been hotly debated for many years. Debate raged as to the value that should be ascribed to travel for different journey purposes (e.g. work or leisure), and whether small time savings for large numbers of passengers could be aggregated. In 1979 the Department of Transport[3] produced, in conjunction with consultants, a definitive study of these *Values Of Time.*

In connection with the planning of rail services, it has been shown[11] that travel time savings on long distance journeys are highly valued by those making the trips, especially where the trips are on employers' business. The valuation of travel time savings was shown to vary significantly depending upon the methodology adopted in measuring the savings. The values arising from the study show long distance rail travellers to value time savings at between 15.5 and 17.4 pence per

Year	Capital Const. Costs	Rolling Stock Costs	Op'ting Costs	Addnl. Rev.	TOTAL Cash Flow	Pass. Time Saved	Benefit Crowd Relief	Road User Benefit	TOTAL Benefit
0	-200	0	0	0	-200	0	0	0	0
1	-200	-83	0	0	-283	0	0	0	0
2	-200	-83	0	0	-283	0	0	0	0
3	-200	-83	0	0	-283	0	0	0	0
4	-200	-83	0	0	-283	0	0	0	0
5	0	0	-40	39	-1	200	100	33	333
6	0	0	-40	41	1	210	105	35	350
7	0	0	-40	43	3	221	110	36	367
8	0	0	-40	45	5	232	116	38	385
9	0	0	-40	47	7	243	122	40	405
10	0	0	-40	50	10	255	128	42	425
11	0	0	-40	52	12	268	134	44	446
12	0	0	-40	55	15	281	141	46	469
13	0	0	-40	58	18	295	148	49	492
14	0	0	-40	61	21	310	155	51	517
15	0	0	-40	61	21	310	155	51	517
16	0	0	-40	61	21	310	155	51	517
17	0	0	-40	61	21	310	155	51	517
18	0	0	-40	61	21	310	155	51	517
19	0	0	-40	61	21	310	155	51	517
20	0	0	-40	61	21	310	155	51	517
21	0	0	-40	61	21	310	155	51	517
22	0	0	-40	61	21	310	155	51	517
23	0	0	-40	61	21	310	155	51	517
24	0	0	-40	61	21	310	155	51	517
25	0	0	-40	61	21	310	155	51	517
26	0	0	-40	61	21	310	155	51	517
27	0	0	-40	61	21	310	155	51	517
28	0	0	-40	61	21	310	155	51	517
29	0	0	-40	61	21	310	155	51	517
30	0	1	-40	61	22	310	155	51	518
NPV	-862	-273	-318	417	-1036	2138	1069	353	3560

Benefit: Cost Ratio 3.43: 1.

In determining the NPV of the cash flows an 8% discount rate has been assumed.

Note the need to replace stock after 30 years, and the residual value of the fleet from the tranche of stock shown (which has a life of 30 years).

Calculation of an Internal Rate of Return is inappropriate here as the total cash flow is negative.

Assumes passenger demand increases for 10 years after opening.

Table 21.1 Example of Appraisal Methodology: Assessing the Costs and Benefits of a New Line.

minute (1984 prices) when converted to the Department of Transport wage rate approach.

Railways tend to use values derived from such studies as showing passenger benefits, and translate these into the additional revenue earned using the elasticity with respect to fares or time. Depending upon the railway this will produce real revenue of between a third and five sixths of the passenger benefits (elasticity values of between -0.7 (elastic) and -0.16 (inelastic)). Off peak and leisure traffic is quite elastic and therefore a great deal of passenger benefits need to be generated, whereas this is not the case for the inelastic commuter.

Attention also needs to be paid to the *"annualisation"* or *Grossing-Up Factor (GUF)* used to factor up estimated values to those appertaining to a whole year. Commonly (e.g. with the network models described in chapter 9), demand estimates will be made for one a.m. peak, and a suitable GUF will be required to estimate an annual figure. With 250 working days, and two peaks each, this value rarely falls below 500. However, offpeak traffic levels vary very considerably (depending upon the competitive environment), and whilst 800 or so may be usual, values of as high as 1300 have been suggested in the London context for lines with good penetration into the main Central shopping and entertainment areas. As the diference between a GUF of 800 and one of 1300 is equivalent to the entire annual peak demand, this has a significant effect on project viability, although it is an under-researched subject.

With a project-based approach it is not difficult to make assessments of the 'hard' values arising from a project, e.g. cost and staff savings over the life of the project. However, some variables are not constant across the life of a project. Demand may take several years to build up to its full value (with only 50-60% of the final figure being applicable in the first year). Costs may change over time; in particular, the concept of the *'bath-tub curve'* (see Figure 21.1) is important for locomotives and rolling stock where, after initial unreliability, maintenance requirements (and hence costs) fall sharply before beginning a long but slow rise towards the expected stock life.

As a clear picture builds up of the various streams of cash flows, discounting can take place to bring all the future and previous flows back to a common base. The principle of discounting therefore allows for the time value of money to be taken into consideration.

Cost : Benefit Analysis (CBA)

We have already seen the basis on which a financial appraisal is carried out. However, for governmental organisations, this is not necessarily

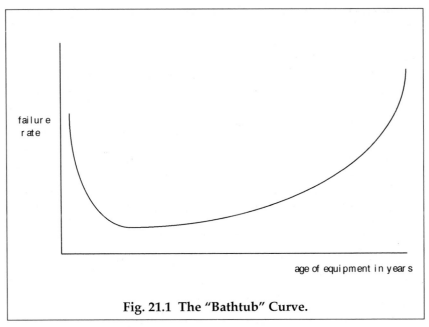

Fig. 21.1 The "Bathtub" Curve.

the most appropriate measure of scheme "worthwhileness". A government may wish to consider other benefits to society e.g. reductions in accidents (which generally occurs if traffic is switched from road to the safer rail mode), time savings to passengers (beyond those which they are willing to pay for), decreases in road congestion (which may obviate the need for new road construction), and so on. Cost : Social Benefit Analysis (CBA) was originally introduced as a concept in Foster and Beesley's seminal papers[5,6] and is now widely used.

CBA follows the same discounting concepts as strict financial appraisal, but there are more benefits (see Table 21.1). Schemes are generally deemed worthwhile if their discounted benefits are 1.3 times their discounted costs; this factor is taken to allow for the marginal return through giving extra subsidy[7], as any scheme with benefits greater than costs should be carried out. The non-financial benefits can be extremely significant in new rail construction, which tends to be very expensive; an analysis of scheme results in the Central London Rail Study[4] showed that non-financial benefits were of the order of five times the financial ones. This ratio is larger than usual, because of the congested nature of London's central-area roads, and also because the

234

schemes were designed to address the relief of overcrowding, which does not in itself generate much additional revenue; perhaps a ratio of two is more usual.

Internal Refinement Process

The internal refinement process is taking the case from "the back of the envelope" through to the point of final approval. The stages here are usually defined as the feasibility studies, main study and authorisation. The processes on railways in the UK usually mean that before a plan or project is taken very far it needs a formal definition. This was a finding of the MMC study of Network South East sector of BR. Projects were found to be ill defined and the recommendation was that prior to the feasibility stage the project be formally defined[12].

A feasibility study should examine a wide range of options and show which (if any) of the options meet the business case (sometimes known as the preferred options). Main studies should take options meeting the business case and refine those which seem most promising. However this tends to induce inertia of the type which says "we did it this way in the past and it worked and therefore that is what we wanted now". This problem can be overcome by the use of written specifications. These set out in broad terms what is required to serve customer needs. The specification might say "rolling stock is required to have a ride index between x and y"; a good specification is one that is easy to measure against well understood parameters.

If a horse was required, once it has gone through the internal refinement process it usually looks like a camel! Therefore projects required to be "edited back into the horse" before it is finally submitted for authorisation. Internally, the authorisation of a project will be made by a committee who will be stewards of the railways budget and expenditure. Many of the smaller projects will be delegated to an individual manager or group of managers to authorise with only the larger projects being considered by the committee[14].

Analysis and Selection of Projects

The analysis and selection of projects needs to be carried out on a consistent basis using consistent criteria. This might include criteria such as the value of time, effects of a delay in cost terms or other conventions such as the nature of analysis (financial or CBA). Until recently in the UK most BR rail schemes were assessed only on a financial basis. There has been a relaxation of this rule particularly where the rail scheme impacts on traffic congestion in urban areas. LUL have since the early 1960's been able to consider the wider societal benefits which may flow from any of their schemes[5,6].

A major recommendation from the Monopolies and Mergers Commission study of LUL[13] was that they should "make more systematic use of information on cost benefit ratios and the financial impact of projects in arriving at its project priority ranking...". Whilst a project may "wash its face" in financial or cost benefit terms it does not guarantee that it will be done, or more importantly, done within a particular timescale, because of funding availability constraints.

Authorisation of Expenditure
Railways in Western Europe are generally state owned or state controlled. Urban railways and light rail systems may be state owned but are more likely to be municipally- or regionally-controlled. However, the ultimate authorisation for expenditure will come from the Government. As Governments usually have significant control over national, regional and municipal expenditure, the procedure described here follows the nationalised industry pattern, although any privatised railway will presumably follow a similar process with its bankers. Although we often read of the Secretary of State for Transport authorising expenditure for new rolling stock or a new line, the Minister will only have made the decision after his civil servants have examined the scheme, usually in great detail[10].

Because of the character of Government funding, the authorisation of railway projects tends to be related to the life of the Government. It has been suggested that the longer life of French Governments may have been a positive influence in the authorisation of major new Ligne a Grande Vitesse lines (LGVs); the life of a French Government can be seven years compared with a maximum of five years in the UK.

It comes as no surprise that BR, LUL and the PTE's have at various times asserted that funding for rail needs to be put on to a longer term basis and with these organisations having clearer objectives to meet. Indeed the MMC report on LUL noted that LUL was "faced with conflicting objectives to an unusual degree". The MMC recommended that a framework for objectives should be agreed by the end of 1991 and that LUL should "prepare a new strategic plan and that it should seek firm political commitment to this plan" (in contrast to the previous 1988 strategic plan).

As noted above, financing limitations are very important. Certainly, in the UK periodic limitations on government capital support of nationalised industries have played havoc with railway investment decisions. There are two financial short term controls placed on the UK's railways. They are respectively the External Financing Limit (EFL) and the Investment and Financing Review (IFR). These two measures

236

cover only the following three years' expenditure. Indications are given as to the likely expenditure in the following two years, but the railways may not commit more than 85% of the indication for the second year or 70% for the third year.

The EFL is equivalent to any grant made plus any borrowing plus net liquid funds (the difference between the opening and closing balances). The IFR covers all nationalised industries and the Government indicates each autumn the level of funds available for the following three financial years which start in April each year.

A major problem arising from such short term control of finances by the stakeholder is that during periods of capital rationing, underfunding (not giving as much funding as is required to do the job safely, efficiently or effectively) may occur. The MMC report on LUL[13] and statements by BR[1] both state that underfunding has occurred in the past. If accidents such as the Kings Cross fire and the signalling failure at Clapham are not to recur, the issue of underfunding must be addressed.

Post Implementation Review

Post Implementation Review follows the completion of the project when the project has been running for some time. The purpose of review is to look at the project and determine by appraisal methods whether the project is being successful or not. In doing so it is useful to highlight problem areas that were encountered during the project (e.g. cost increases and time delays) and why they occurred, and to disseminate the results widely to try and ensure that future projects do not become afflicted in a similar way. If the benefits of a project have been achieved this can be reflected either in a changed budget with lower costs or increased revenue. By the achievement of such benefits the railway will move towards its own organisational goals.

Conclusions

The railway investment process is not particularly complicated. It is a matter of following certain rules to satisfy the stakeholder that funds are spent effectively, efficiently and in a safe matter. The procedures set out how the project will be appraised and set the passmarks to be achieved. At the end of the process lessons need to be learned from reviewing how projects have been achieved, whether the budget and timescales were met and the benefits or cost savings achieved.

References
1. British Railways Board (1991) "Future Rail - The Next Decade".
2. Department of the Environment (1974) "London Rail Study", HMSO.

3. Department of Transport & The MVA Consultancy (1987) "The Value of Time", Policy Journals, Newbury.
4. Department of Transport, British Rail Network SouthEast, London Regional Transport and London Underground Ltd. (1989) "Central London Rail Study".
5. Foster, C.D. & Beesley M.E. (1963) "Estimating the Social Benefit of Constructing an Underground Railway in London', *Jnl. Royal Stat. Soc.* 126 pp. 46-58.
6. Foster, C.D. & Beesley M.E. (1965) "Victoria Line: Social Benefit and Finances" *Jnl. Royal Stat. Soc.* pp. 72 - 73.
7. Glaister, S. (1987) "Allocation of Urban Public Transport Subsidy", pp. 26-39 in "Transport Subsidy" (ed. Glaister), Policy Journals, Newbury.
8. Godward, E. (1987) "Return to Snow Hill", *Modern Rlys.* pp. 533-538.
9. Godward, E. (1990) "Cross City Electrification", *Modern Rlys.* pp. 643-647.
10. Irvine, K. (1989) "Finance for Railway Development" World Rail - Service and Profit, Financial Times Conferences, London.
11. Marks, P., Fowkes, A. S. and Nash, C. (1987) "Valuing Long Distance Business Travel Time Savings For Evaluation: A Methodological Review and Application", PTRC Conference.
12. Monopolies and Mergers Commission. (1988) "British Rail: Network South East".
13. Monopolies and Mergers Commission (1991) "London Underground Limited: A report on Passenger and Other Services Supplied by the Company", HMSO, London, Cmnd.1555.
14. Perren, B. (1991) "Managing British Rail", *Rail* 157 pp.26-28.
15. Semmens, P. (1991) "Electrifying the East Coast Route: The making of Britains first 140mph railway", Patrick Stephens Ltd (Sparkford), 224pp.
16. Stewart, V. & Chadwick, V. (1987) "Changing Trains", David & Charles, Newton Abbot, p. 139.

A useful and easily readable text on the subject of appraisal is "Investment Appraisal: A Guide for Managers" by Rob Dixon and published by Kogan Page Professional Paperbacks in association with the Chartered Institute of Management Accountants. Some of the references in chapter 2 also show how railways interact with their sponsoring Governments.

22. The Future of Passenger Railways

Ernest Godward

Introduction

Throughout the world, railways are back in the ascendency. They are seen to provide a safe, efficient means of transport with minimal environmental impact. The main reasons for this are fourfold:-

1. Increasing demand for transport;
2. Increasing road congestion;
3. Increasing concern over environmental matters; and
4. Technology-led cost reductions.

The demand for transport is a derived demand; few people travel for the sake of it. As the economy grows so will the demand for transport in the economy grow. Many countries, both in the developed and developing worlds, are finding that rail transport is cost effective at meeting some of the growth in demand through the construction of new lines or more effective and efficient use of existing lines and services.

The passenger railway is providing a major response to curbing the problems caused by the growth in urban areas. The world becomes ever more urban. The growth of cities in many parts of the world has caused similar growth in car ownership. Many urban areas are building new rail links both on the surface and underground to cater for mass transit demands that the car cannot meet.

Developments in control methods, operations and new forms of rolling stock have led to the renaissance of railways in rural areas as costs have been reduced. Whilst operating techniques are developing, many passenger railways still do not cover their costs. Governments are now seeking solutions to this problem, perhaps by changes in railway organisation, but as yet only two have faced the problem and sought a solution (see chapter 10).

The Interurban Passenger Railway

The modern railway in its high speed interurban form has perhaps had the most significant impact on the general public's perception of railways. The most significant incarnations have been the Japanese

Fig. 22.1 Photo of the TGV Atlantique Interior.

Bullet trains, SNCF's Train a Grande Vitesse (TGV) (see Fig. 22.1) and recently DB's Inter City Express (ICE).

In 1990 the future of long distance passenger railways was boosted through a new world rail speed record of 515.3 km/hr (320 miles per hour) by TGV set 325[1]. The SNCF have shown that with a specially engineered track between major centres and a performance train it is possible to produce a commercially viable railway with good profit returns. The French Government approved a plan submitted by SNCF in 1990 to establish a 4440 kilometre network of TGV lines[5]. This plan is estimated to cost £21 billion at current prices, and will include lines where there is a low rate of return. The French Government is expecting local communities along the routes to make contributions in order to achieve the required rates of return. At the same time the SNCF announced that it had placed orders worth £1 billion for a redesigned double deck train to cope with the increases in passenger demand on the Paris - Sud-Est route. The first of the 45 trains will be delivered in 1994.

In the UK the Intercity 125 High Speed Train provided a significant development on conventional rail routes. The ideas developed in the mid 1970's for the Advanced Passenger Train have been further developed and refined in the electrically powered Intercity 225. The Intercity 225 is now operating on BR's East Coast Main Line and a planned Intercity 250 train for the modernised and upgraded West Coast Main Line is expected.

The development of the high speed interurban railway has taken advantage of the significant developments associated with the power and signalling electronics that have occurred since the 1950's. These developments have enabled speeds to increase to over 250 km/hr for the fastest trains. It is likely that further developments will be oriented towards achieving these speeds with greater efficiency of power. However, it has been argued, in a recent lecture[8], that there are diminishing returns above 250 km/hr.

The Passenger Railway in the Urban Environment

The requirement of passenger railways (including light rail) in urban areas is to move the greatest numbers of passengers safely, at least cost and usually in two peak periods of about three hours. Some cities also have midday peaks as well although these tend to be less pronounced than the morning and evening peaks.

Current modern metros could have a capacity of up to 32,000 passengers per hour with standard rolling stock. For example, London Underground, which is currently modernising its Central Line, has used a planning target of 31,500 passengers per hour per track. The modernised line will have a modern signalling system capable of passing trains at headways of 1.7 minutes under manual train operation. In France, however, the Paris Transport Authority RATP are experimenting with new double decked regional express metro rolling stock which could raise the capacity of a single track to 54,000 passengers per hour; an example of double-deck stock is shown in Fig. 22.2.

In the last 20 years many cities have had to build new urban railway lines. Increases in the ownership of cars has caused congestion to rise significantly. Large cities such as Los Angeles, where car ownership is extremely high and where the structure of the city is polycentric (consisting of many centres) have suffered from the 'gridlock' phenomenon. Accidents or incidents cause the road system to grind to a halt. This prolongs journey times significantly, increasing car produced gaseous pollution and noise levels. Cities such as this are quickly re-introducing rail based transit systems as they offer relief from such problems.

New railways may help solve other urban problems such as the regeneration of older, run-down or derelict districts of a city (e.g. the

Fig. 22.2 SNCF Double-Deck Stock on Lille Urban Service.

Jubilee line and Docklands Light Railway in London, and the Sheffield Light Rail System (see chapter 4)). New railways can also help to provide new opportunities for employment by increasing accessibility for urban residents.

Rural Passenger Railways

In the past the normal response had been to close lines where costs did not meet revenues. In the 1960's and 1970's in the UK many routes fell victim to the accountant's axe. Similar actions were taken in Europe in the 1970's but the closures were not on such a scale as they were in the UK. However, political change, consumer action groups and a better understanding of the way in which rural rail routes contribute revenue to main lines have meant that when routes have come up for closure, considerable doubts have been expressed; Table 7.1 shows that many fewer lines are now being closed.

The consequences of passenger railway closures were highlighted in a study by the Policy Studies Institute published in 1980[4]. The study showed that buses were inadequate substitutes for rail. The overall use of the remaining rail system was lower for those affected by the closures. Inadequate powers of County Councils concerning railways had not helped matters. The closure of rural railways was seen as

242

socially regressive affecting the old, those without cars, women and those from blue-collar households.

Simpler infrastructure for rural railways and radio signalling systems coupled with fewer and more multifunctioned staff has led to the survival of a large number of rural routes. In Europe radio signalling is common on many rural lines. The line controller/signalman arranges for crossings on single lines and organises local control through the use of available staff by radio. In the north of Holland, Nederlands Spoorwegen (NS) has brought in rail-cars where the driver also acts as conductor selling tickets to passengers as they board.

In Scotland and Wales many single lines are operated safely with radio electronic token block signalling. This ties in the use of computerised signalling with radio used to transmit the signals from a centralised control centre to remote trains.

Traction and Motive Power

There are essentially two forms of motive power for passenger railways; electric and diesel. In urban areas and on main interurban routes traction power will come from overhead electric or rail side conductors. On rural and less heavily trafficked routes diesel power usually predominates.

In the wake of the electronics revolution in the mid 1950's railway engineering companies have sought to make use of such developments for controlling tractive power. Todays modern electric locomotives and multiple units intended for passenger service tend to have high power to weight ratios. Reductions in weight or increases in power are useful in that these can be help to improve services for passengers through more capacity, higher acceleration rates or higher speeds.

Diesel technology has also benefited from the electronics revolution. Diesel-electric control has been able to take advantage of the benefits of power electronics whilst diesel-mechanical power has used new engine developments to improve multiple unit fleets. In the UK and Denmark high speed diesel units are able to offer high quality accommodation and services along with higher speeds (between 145km/h to 180km/h for the latest designs).

The future for traction appears to be in developing traction control systems that optimise power required and that are simple to maintain. In addition the power control components must not interfere with other systems such as signalling. As knowledge and understanding have increased so the numbers of components required have been reduced. Table 22.1, showing numbers of gate turn off (GTO) thyristors on locomotives, illustrates this very well.

Locomotive type	Drive	Year	Number of devices	Power MW
SNCF BB15000	DC	1971	136	4.6
BR 87101	DC	1973	128	3.6
BR APT Prototype	DC	1974	40	5.7
BR 91 Class	DC	1988	28	4.7
SNCF BB10004	Synchronous	1982	132	4.6
SNCF BB26000 Class	Synchronous	1987	96	5.6
DB 120 Class	Asynchronous	1983	450	5.6
SNCF BB10003	Asynchronous	1983	350	4.6

Table 22.1 Comparison of thyristor drive systems for railway locomotives (Source: ref. 7)

Whole-life costs of locomotives and multiple units have been reduced as a result of the introduction of GTO thyristors, which have enabled the replacement of costly electro-mechanical equipment. Coupled with the use of microprocessors, the use of power semiconductors will enable the simplification of power systems and the containment of costs in the long run. It is likely that the use of AC drives will also become much more common as these too allow further simplification leading to long run cost reductions.

Signalling, Control and Operation
The modern railway signalling and control centre is a far cry from the old mechanical signal boxes. Even in the 1990's mechanical signal boxes still remain, but increasingly they are confined to secondary lines. Given investment in signalling and control methods the mechanical instruments of 19th and early 20th Century origin are likely to be replaced with radio or transmission based systems controlled by computer.

Modern signalling systems rely heavily on the use of information technology. The signalling control centre not only provides the signalling function but provides the passengers and management with train running information. Software and control systems are increasingly "artificially intelligent" and have the ability to suggest or take a course of action based on given rule sets.

The use of electronics and computers has led to the much safer operation of passenger railways. Modern electronics and software can overcome many of the failings of previous mechanical systems. New systems are more likely to be an integrated system not only protecting the track on which the train is routed but also providing a degree of control over the train itself. Designers of such systems build in a level of redundancy to ensure that where failures do occur the system can operate safely or fail safe. In modern computer controlled signal interlockings this takes the form of three processors with at least two having to be in agreement; any less and the system "fails safe".

Infrastructure

The major development here has been the development of track and infrastructure forms which allow high speeds with minimal maintenance. Many railways now use flat bottomed long welded rail. This is easily maintained by mechanical means. The railway supply industry has produced a wide variety of machines from tampers and liners to the dynamic track stabilisers. The latter allow the use of newly laid line at or near line speeds immediately after track has been laid and stabilised. Such mechanisation has helped reduce overall costs.

On electrification projects the used of specialised equipment has significantly reduced the time taken to install catenary and masts. In 1974 it had taken 59 months for the completion of 225 route miles between Weaver Junction and Glasgow, averaging 3.8 route miles per month compared with 4.7 route miles per month for the recently completed East Coast mainline (382 route miles in 82 months). This equates to a 24% improvement in productivity.

Developments in civil engineering have led to bridges built in lightweight materials with strength equivalent to steel or iron. New methods have also featured in bridge construction; like a model kit they are simply glued together.

Marketing

Without marketing the railways would probably carry fewer passengers. Railway administrations have long realised that while they may offer a fast journey time, they may not be able to compete with the car for convenience or aircraft over longer distances. The railway administrations must therefore market their passenger services.

Passenger railways, world-wide, have assumed the perspective of the consumer. Many railways have become, or are in the process of becoming, business-led, rather than production-led, organisations. They aim to provide the needs of the buyer or potential buyer with the services they offer. In order to do this many passenger railway organisations have had to adapt information from management sources or commission the collection of separate passenger information. Understanding this information has required more sophisticated research procedures, and this has given new insights into passengers' travel behaviour.

The rail administration then needs to restructure or repackage the service or products they offer based on the research. In order for the changes to be successful the changes need to be communicated to the users and potential users. When new products and services have been implemented or changed the success or otherwise needs to be monitored in both quantitative and qualitative terms. The quantitative will show the change in passengers and revenues derived from them whilst the qualitative monitoring will show the levels of awareness and attitudes towards them[9].

Marketing is not only selling or advertising; it is a whole concept encompassing market research to public relations. The marketing function should be able to translate the plans of the railway into understandable communication with the staff, press, users and non users of the railway.

Accountability

We have already seen in chapter 10 that there has been a recent change in attitude towards the management of operations, with the aims of focussing more clearly on the task in hand, and in providing better value for money for the taxpayer (where appropriate). In addition to this, several governments are considering railway privatisation in one of its various forms, although care must be taken to distinguish between changes in ownership and changes in structure. The options for changes in structure are perhaps as follows:

1. business-led (an extension of current British practice);
2. regional (as in Japan[6]);
3. splitting off operations only, with responsibility for infrastructure remaining with the State (as in Sweden).

It would also be possible to change ownership without changing structure; in this so-called plc approach, the railway might be sold off en bloc, as several other former nationalised undertakings have been in the UK.

It is difficult to speculate in this area. In Europe all of the above options might occur simultaneously, as each nation state views the role of the railway in a different way. In the UK, the plc and business sector approaches find favour with those who would wish to see the railways out of the public sector, but many railway staff would prefer to remain working in a nationalised industry. The European Commission[3] (supported by Britain's House of Lords[6]) certainly favour greater access to Europe's rail network, whilst protecting socially-necessary services by clearly-understood grants or contracts for services operated under market discipline.

Concluding Remarks

It was Dr. Richard Beeching who said "The profitability or otherwise of a railway system is dependent on a number of external influences which may change markedly from time to time, important among them being decisions affecting the freedom of use, cost of use and availability of roads. For this and other reasons, it is impossible to plan the maximum use of railways consistent with profitability, for years ahead, without some risk that it will prove in the event, that services have been over-provided and that overall profitability is not achieved. On the other hand, to retain only those parts of the existing system which are virtually certain to be self-supporting under any reasonable probable future conditions would lead to a grave risk of destroying assets which, in the event, might have proved valuable."[2] Whatever one thinks of Beeching, he realised that railways were required to meet part of the total transport requirement for a country. In order to do that effectively a plan was required.

In this book we have set out to show how passenger railways are planned. It is a passenger railways' ability to plan for, and subsequently, execute change that will secure its future. Railway planning has developed much recently. It is to be hoped that this book will contribute to the process and to the continued success of passenger railways as a form of transport.

References

1. Anon (1990) "French Blast TGV up to 515.3km/h", *Railway Gaz. Intnl.* 146 p. 411.
2. British Railways Board (1963) "The Reshaping of British Railways", HMSO, London, pp. 2-3.
3. EC Communication on a Community Railway Policy. 4478/90 COM(89)564.
4. Hillman, M. & Whalley, A. (1980) "The Social Consequences of Rail Closures", Report 587, Policy Studies Institute, London.
5. Hope, R. (1990) "SNCF Weaves its High Speed Web", *Railway Gaz. Intnl.* 146 pp. 851-855.
6. House of Lords (1990) "A New Structure for Community Railways", HL Paper 11, HMSO, London.
7. Kemp, R.J. (1989) "Developments in Electric Traction", *Power Engng. Jnl.* pp. 71-82.
8. Prideaux, J.D.C.A. (1989) "InterCity: Passenger Railway Without Subsidy", Lecture given to the Royal Society of Arts, London, 24th May.
9. Prowda, R.M. & Draeger, R. (1984) "Defining the Market and Selling the Product", University of Nottingham Public Transport Conference.
10. Suga, T. (1988) "The Privatisation of Japanese National Railways", INRETS Road Transport conference.

Biographical Details of Contributors

Editors

Nigel G Harris read Geography at Durham University, concentrating on British economic geography. He then carried out research into two-tier fares policy with BR's erstwhile Provincial sector whilst studying for his PhD at the University of Newcastle-upon-Tyne. Following that, he worked for consultants MVA, first in demand modelling for London Underground's Central Line Project, and subsequently on the LTS model. Since then, he has been LUL's Network Analyst, providing advice to senior managers whilst the company has changed significantly - including as a result of the 1988 Strategic Plan.

Ernest Godward graduated from Aston University with a Combined Honours degree in Transport Planning and Operation and Urban Planning. As well as having worked for consultancies such as Colin Buchanan and Partners and the Economic Studies Group, he spent five years as the head of the market research unit at West Midlands PTE. Following that he was a senior lecturer at the City of Birmingham Polytechnic, where he taught and researched economics, econometrics and transport policy. He is now a financial appraisal specialist at London Underground (responsible for both financial and economic assessments of LUL's extensive capital programme), but is currently seconded onto a management team developing a Company Plan for LUL.

Contributors

Hugh Sumner is a Chartered Engineer by training, and also has an MBA from Cranfield. He has held a wide variety of line and staff roles across a number of industries including civil engineering, consulting and transportation. Within London Underground, he was a key member of the 1988 Strategic Plan team, which culminated in his being appointed as General Manager of the Bakerloo line. A subsequent return to a staff role sees him in charge of devolution of maintenance to the lines, and as a core member of the latest corporate change programme including formulation of the 1991 Company Plan.

Phil Haywood is Director of Planning with South Yorkshire Passenger Transport Executive (SYPTE). He joined SYPTE in 1985 and has been responsible for such tasks as the development and modernisation of passenger facilities, and coordinating the application to the UK Department of Transport for grant for Sheffield's Supertram light rail system. Before joining SYPTE, he was with West Midlands PTE for 10 years, where he was responsible for developing the new organisation's market research and monitoring capability. Prior to that, he started his career after graduating from London University with British Rail, where he was involved with corporate planning and market research for the passenger business.

Rob Sheldon has 15 years transportation research experience encompassing three consultancies - MVA, SDG and now, as Managing Director of Accent marketing and Research Ltd. During this period he has managed several

248

hundred projects for clients throughout the world. A substantial proportion of these have involved stated preference techniques, upon which subject he is an expert, having delivered over twenty papers at major conferences. Rob also co-directs a bi-monthly course on new product developments for th Chartered Institute of Marketing, where he lectures on the use and value of market research approaches.

Jonathan Preston graduated from Nottingham University in 1981 and moved to the Institute for Transport Studies at Leeds University in 1982. He studied for a PhD on the Evaluation of New Local Rail Stations in West Yorkshire, which was awarded in 1987. This research has continued with over a dozen grants, whilst he has also been involved in monitoring the effects of bus deregulation. He is currently the British Rail sponsored lecturer in Transport Economics at the Institute.

Malcolm Buchanan is a director of Colin Buchanan and Partners, who are planning, transport and economics consultants. He was formerly head of the GLC's rail planning section, and has recently acted as advisor to the Department of Transport on public transport in the London area. He was appointed by LB Newham in 1988 to examine the case for a Channel Tunnel terminal at Stratford.

Robert Cochrane has over twenty years' experience in the planning, design and management of freight, mixed traffic and mass transit railway systems in the UK, Australia and Hong Kong. Major projects with which he has been associated include the Channel Tunnel, the Hong Kong Mass Transit Railway and the Australian Railway Standardisation Programme. He spent five years as a senior manager with British Rail, where he held the posts of Investment Adviser to the Board, and InterCity Resource and Planning Director. His most recent work at consultants Putnam, Hayes and Bartlett has been the development and analysis of alternative organisational structures for rail privatisation.

David Haydock graduated from Aston University with a Combined Honours degree in Transport Planning and Operation and Urban Planning. He worked for consultants Colin Buchanan and Partners, and the Crosville Bus Company before moving to Merseyside PTE where he planned bus and rail networks. In 1984 he moved to France, and has written extensively about European railway operations, including publishing a number of books. He is currently the European correspondent for Rail magazine.

Tom Greaves held the post of British Rail Board Traction and Train Crew Manager between 1980 and 1988. During this period he undertook a key role in a number of significant initiatives in improving train crew productivity, including career progressions, flexible rostering and driver-only operation. He is now the Managing Director of Traction Consult, a firm specialising in such personnel activities.

David Catling held senior posts with London Transport in rolling stock development, maintenance, training and project management, including consultancy assignments in Singapore, South America and Dublin. Latterly he was made responsible for developing new lower-cost rail systems, and became Engineering Manager of the new Docklands Light Railway. He is now a consultant and writer, with a special interest in the planning and optimisation of new light rail schemes.

Roger Ford trained as an engineer with English Electric and joined the Company's Traction Division on qualification. In 1966 he left the railway industry for a career in technical publicity, returning in 1976 to become Technical Editor of Modern Railways. Since then he has written on technical, commercial and operating subjects for this and other leading railway publications.

Tony M Ridley CBE holds the Rees Jeffreys Chair in Transport Engineering at London University, within the Department of Civil Engineering at Imperial College.

He joined the Board of Eurotunnel as a non-executive member in 1987, and was Managing Director of the project from 1989 until 1990. Immediately prior to that he spent eight years with London Transport, joining as Managing Director of London's underground system in 1980. He was appointed Chairman and Managing Director (later Chief Executive) of London Underground Ltd. when it was created in 1985. He was a member of the Board of London Regional Transport (London Underground's parent company), and was also Chairman of two other LRT subsidiary companies, Docklands Light Railway Ltd. and London Transport International.

He was Managing Director of the Hong Kong Mass Transit Railway Corporation from 1975-1980, and was the first Director General of the Tyne and Wear Passenger Transport Executive from 1969-1975.

He holds a Doctorate in Transportation Engineering from the University of California as well as civil engineering degrees from the University of Newcastle-upon-Tyne and Northwestern University. He attended the Senior Executive Program at Stanford Business School in 1980.

He is a Fellow of both the Chartered Institute of Transport (of which he has been Vice President, and is currently Chairman of the Transport Policy Committee) and of the Institution of Civil Engineers (of which he is a Member of Council and Chairman of the Transport Engineering Board). He is President of the Light Rail Transit Association. He has been active in the International Union of Public Transport, and is now its Advisor on EC Affairs. In 1988 he was the first recipient of the Highways Award of the Institution of Highways and Transportation.

Don Box was employed on cost research work for British Rail from the late 1950s until full-time retirement in 1984, and was involved in designing many of the changes in costing practice which took place during that time. More recently he has advised foreign railways on costing practices. At present he is working on the revision of BR's infrastructure costing systems. The impact of government policy on the development of costing practices as opposed to theory is of particular interest to him.

Stuart Cole is Director of Transport Research and Consultancy (TRaC) and Director of Transport Courses at the Polytechnic of North London Business School. He is the author of "Applied Transport Economics", the CIT-recommended text for its transport economics course, and is a co-author of three other books. He has written over forty articles, made over 250 broadcasts on radio and television, and contributed to articles in national newspapers on transport economics and policy, and environmental issues. He has carried out numerous research and consultancy projects in these fields. Since 1984 he has advised the House of Commons Select Committee on Welsh Affairs on ten enquiries into transport issues in Cymru/Wales. Prior to joining PNL in 1979, he was Economic Adviser in the Transportation Unit at Cheshire County Council.

Ben Thanacanamootoo was educated in Mauritius and graduated from the Indian Institute of Technology, Kanpur in 1981. He obtained his PhD in 1987 from the University of Newcastle-upon-Tyne, where his research study was on the impact of noise from urban railway operations, using the Tyne and Wear Metro as his case-study. From 1986 to 1988, he worked as a Research Associate at the University on automatic incident detection in urban areas. He is currently employed with consultants Transportation Planning Associates in Birmingham.

Michael Schabas is an indepedent consultant specialising in planning, design, finance and implementation of rapid transit systems. He was responsible for design coordination of the Vancouver Skytrain, was Chief Planner for the Honolulu rapid transit project, and is in charge of transport planning for the Canary Wharf developers in London Docklands. He has also led international marketing efforts for a major rail system manufacturer and is currently advising on rail projects on two continents. He has a degree in Architecture from the University of Toronto and a Masters from the J.F.Kennedy School of Government at Harvard.

Index